Not Deaf Enough:
Raising a Child
Who is Hard of Hearing
with Hugs, Humor, and Imagination

The Candlish Family. Left to Right: Reid (Our Hero), Tiffany, PAM, William and Barbara
Photo by Ross Candlish

Not Deaf Enough: Raising a Child Who is Hard of Hearing with Hugs, Humor, and Imagination

by Patricia Ann Morgan Candlish, M.L.S.

Alexander Graham Bell
Association for the Deaf, Inc.
3417 Volta Place, N.W. 20007-2778

Library of Congress Cataloging in Publication Data

Candlish, Patricia Ann Morgan, M.L.S.
Not Deaf Enough: Raising a Child Who Is Hard of Hearing with Hugs, Humor and Imagination.

Library of Congress Catalog Card Number 94-71624
ISBN-0-88200-201-5
© 1996 Alexander Graham Bell Association for the Deaf, Inc.
3417 Volta Place, N.W.
Washington, D.C. 20007-2778

Printed in the United States of America

10 9 8 7 6 5 4 3 2 1

Contents

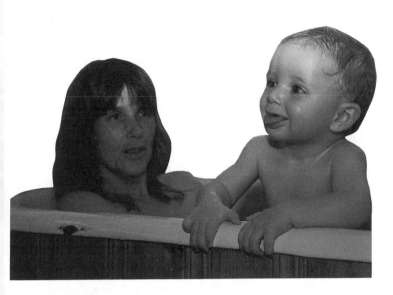

Introduction

If you become a rock on the mountain high above me . . . I will be a mountain climber and I will climb to where you are. If you become a crocus in a hidden garden . . . I will be a gardener and I will find you.

Margaret Wise Brown, *The Runaway Bunny*

Not Deaf Enough: Raising a Child Who Is Hard of Hearing is the story of my child Reid, who is hard of hearing, a child whose better ear hearing loss is relatively mild. At age two, he was first labelled "Not Deaf Enough" by a professional assessing him. Like most children with similar hearing problems, his hearing loss is often ignored, underestimated and misunderstood by the world at large. *Not Deaf Enough* is also the story of many other children with varied hearing problems, their parents, and the professionals who work with them.

It began sitting in a dark room with Reid on my knee. Someone had just said, "Your baby has a hearing problem." We wondered, "What does that mean?"

Not much is written about the child who is hard of hearing, especially those with mild or moderate hearing losses. Children with these problems can easily fall between the cracks because they are not "profoundly deaf." However, a child who is hard of hearing faces life-disrupting problems and meets many daily challenges. The child's parents may grieve for the hearing loss and worry about the child's future in the same way as parents of children with more severe hearing problems. The siblings are expected to love and accept a family member who has a problem.

I believe parents need information about everything to do with a hearing problem, and then they can begin to help the child. Good information also prepares the parents to act as advocate for the child with the outside world ... with other children and adults, with teachers, audiologists, doctors and other professionals. This is particularly important for children with mild losses because there are many people out there who still believe "Put hearing aids on the child and he will learn to speak, get straight A's in school and become President." Sure, hearing aids help the child to hear better, but it is only the beginning. Once you understand "why" a child needs hearing aids, and what their limitations are, you can help your child.

It was not the audiologist who crawled on hands and knees around a shopping mall looking for Reid's hearing aid. Nor did Reid ever throw his hearing aids across the room when the itinerant teacher of the deaf was visiting. It was not the auditory-verbal therapist who pushed the swing one thousand times repeating basic speech sounds, although occasionally it was a speech pathologist pushing her own child next to me. Mostly I, Mummy, did the work, but my husband Ross, and Reid's siblings, Tiffany, Barbara, and William also pitched in.

All children who have hearing problems need help from their families. The family does the everyday work that builds language and teaches patterns of "how to behave." Sometimes the families of children who have hearing problems are so busy coping that they lose their sense of humor, and their intuitive understanding of a child's expectations and accomplishments. Here are things you can learn to do as part of a regular daily routine which make it easier to have a member of the family who is hard of hearing.

The cheapest and best teaching aids are the parent and the family. The ingenuity and natural playfulness of all of you engaged in hours of talking and listening everyday has a remarkable, cumulative effect. The photographs of all of us scattered throughout the book reflect this. This is a family, all active, all learning, doing, playing, talking and listening. Reid was right there in the midst of it, and Reid learned to speak and to listen, and see himself as an important part of the whole. That is how Reid grew up.

PAM Candlish
West Luther, Ontario, Canada 1996

P.S. The arbitrary use of "he" or "she" are done sometimes in the interest of a smooth reading style. The term "Deaf" is used for people and institutions that are in the Deaf Community and for those who use sign language as their primary form of communication.

P.P.-S. The Ling Five-Sounds Test which was used during Reid's learning period is now often known as the Ling Six-Sounds Test with the addition of the **m** sound.

Useful Tips and Thoughts

With the above in mind I have made lists of **Useful Tips and Thoughts** to go at the end of each chapter (at the end of the book). I want this material to repeat information given within the text in an accessible, short form, classified by subject. This can be a reminder for parents and the immediate family and a short, simple way to give essential information for other caretakers, teachers, professionals, grandparents and the outside world.

Acknowledgements

To Dan Ling for reading an early version of the manuscript and encouraging me to continue. Dr. Ling autographed my copy of his new book, "In appreciation of a great parent." He probably says that to all of us who try to do the best for our children. I answer him here:

**In appreciation of a truly great teacher,
Daniel Ling,
who has devoted his life to helping hearing-impaired children to
talk.**

To Judy Simser of *Auditory-Verbal International* who took the manuscript on her summer vacation. And to Lucy Cuzon du Rest, and Don McGee, and Elizabeth Quigley of the *Alexander Graham Bell Association for the Deaf, Inc.* who have graciously put up with phone calls, faxes, and gurgles. Lucy, if this is your swan song, it is a great tune!

To the Itinerant Pre-School Teachers of the Deaf of the *E.C. Drury School for the Deaf* who got us going, to Carol Pavey who listened to us, Catherine McEnroe, our therapist, and Rosemary Pryde of *VOICE for Hearing-Impaired Children* who encouraged us. To Garth Sweet, our Special Education Officer, to James MacDougall of *McGill University*, to Richard Seewald and Shane Moodie of the *University of Western Ontario*, to Ian McIntosh of *Ear Mold Design Ltd*, to Trish Taylor formerly of *Hearing Ear Dogs of Canada* for a day in a dog's training, to Nina Picton of *CHEO*, Riza Razack for educational audiology, to Gay Gretton for speech pathology, to Carol Flexer and all the parents and professionals who took time to talk, read or write. To the *Family Resource Center on Disabilities* for U.S. tax information, and *Bell Canada* for services for the hard of hearing. To Patrick McMullon for photography, to *Phonic Ear* and *Unitron* for illustrations.

To all the people who call and ask, "How's the book?" To Inger Lise, Lars and Bonnie Lilholt. To Marcia Swaby for psychological support and friendship since J.W.R.M. and Willy S. To Sheila Reid, my "Howdy Doody" and "Oreos" friend, To all the people who invented computers and keep making them better, To Ross and Patrick for helping with the computer when Ross could have been mowing the lawn and Patrick could have been playing golf. To Mary-Jean and Hugh Watson who encouraged my education and to Bob Morgan, my brother and pater-familias. To Jan Morgan who took time from her books *A Chronicle of Lower Canada* to correct spelling, dangling participles and other henious English crimes.

To Ross, who read pages of tiny handwriting with excitement and encouragement, to Tiffany who learned to cook so the family would not starve, to Barbara who learned to read to herself, to William who complained that he was not only lacking in quantity time, but was been deprived of quality time too, and to Reid who learned not to unplug the computer when Mummy was typing . . . **Thanks**.

Chapter 1
The Less Than Perfect Baby

Despite what we may see in a mirror, we expect perfection in our children's bodies and abilities. The new mother and father anxiously await a moment of privacy with the newborn child to count fingers and toes, admire genitalia, perfection of eyebrows and tiny delicate ears and noses. My firstborn looked like Nefertiti run over by a truck. Tiffany had bruises on both cheeks and forehead, a prominent storksfoot, a hematoma in one eye and her head only turned one way. My second baby was a breech baby. Barbara had a perfect head right from birth, but her bottom was swollen and pointed. William had to be extricated from the gallows' knot of the cord and was blue. Could a baby be so blue and still be healthy? The first three children were perfect after recovering from the stresses of birth. The last child was not perfect.

In my last month of pregnancy, the car skidded. I had intense Braxton-Hicks contractions the rest of the pregnancy. They squeezed me so hard that I would have to stop talking (most unusual). On my due date, real contractions began. I visited the doctor who said to call when the contractions were down to five minutes. Four days later, I phoned the doctor and announced that the contractions were still going on. The doctor said to meet him at the hospital. The nurses attached a monitor to me and recorded mild contractions and the fact that the baby's heartbeat was dropping after every contraction.

Trapped in a transverse lie, the cord knotted around his neck, swimming in meconium and with the placenta 90 percent detached and putrefying, Reid was born by Caesarian section. His first Apgar (index of vital signs) was *0*, his second *2*, because they got his heart to beat. Eventually the medical team got him to breathe with the aid of a machine and tubes. His first twelve hours of life were critical, going from functioning to non-functioning in all his body systems. Ross stood at the 'critical' nursery window and willed Reid to live. He aged twenty years that day. When Reid's temperature started falling, he was transported to a big city children's hospital. Ross continued his vigil downtown, rejoicing at every positive step and never relenting in the face of despair. Reid is my husband's child because they bonded when I could not.

Nobody advised us about what we could expect. The medical team was so surprised at Reid's survival that anything was counted as successful. Also, I think doctors avoid prognostications which might be emotional and inaccurate. Our family doctor, two years later, told me he had thought Reid would be "retarded," but said nothing at the time. Most of the doctor-patient dialogue time was used up by a "going home" debate. I assumed that the baby was more or less normal, although pathetically thin. I blithely put him into a normal newborn baby routine.

The first night we put Reid to bed and turned out the light. He howled. We turned on the light. He stopped. We turned out the light. He howled again. Of course, being in an intensive care nursery for ten days he had never experienced dark. We told him about going to bed, the sun setting and dark time. Then we turned out the light. He howled. Experienced parents that we were, we told him he had to learn it got dark every single night and left the lights off. Now we realize that dark is much more than visual deprivation, because he has hearing problems. We did not know we were cutting off his contacts with the world. We thought we were teaching him about night and day.

One day, when four-week-old Reid was dozing in a basket on the floor, someone came to the door. The dogs flashed by, barking loudly. I noticed

Reid did not react. On the return trip the hair on the Sheltie's tail just grazed the basket, the baby was startled and cried. I got out some bells and pots, and made noise to see what the baby would do. He did not seem to react. That night Ross and I tried to get the baby to react to sound. Ross was sure he remembered Reid reacting when the alarms went off in the critical care nursery, but he was not reacting now.

At my postpartum appointment, I suggested that the baby might be deaf, and was told, "All mothers think their five-week-old babies are deaf. Just be patient." At Reid's first "well baby" checkup, I suggested the baby might be deaf. The doctor clapped his hands, the baby blinked. The doctor said there did not appear to be a problem. At the next checkup, I repeated my suggestion, the doctor repeated the test and the baby blinked. I said, "I think the baby sees. I don't think he hears." The doctor quoted chapter and verse of something about "startle" (alerting to a sudden stimulus) reactions.

Ross came along on the next checkup, and insisted the baby could not hear. The doctor sounded a tuning fork behind the baby's head. Reid did not blink. Referrals were made to see an ENT (ear, nose and throat doctor) who referred us to a children's ENT. The ENT, on the basis of a tympanogram, (an evaluation of middle ear function) said that Reid should have ventilation tubes and a Brain Stem Auditory Evoked Response Test (BAER) I refused to have tubes put in Reid's ear drums, but allowed a myringotomy (opening the eardrum to allow drainage), to see what might be in his middle ear. We had to wait for operating room time.

The audiologist came to see us after the BAER and said, "I'm sorry to have to tell you, but your son, Brock, has a mild/severe hearing loss." The baby was thrashing around in my arms coming out of the anesthetic and I corrected her, "My child's name is not Brock, it is Reid." The audiologist said, "Oh, yes, Reid . . . Brock has 'solid' in his middle ears which was . . ." I corrected the name again. She said, "Yes, Reid . . . Brock has middle ear problems (glue ear) but the doctor removed what he could during the myringotomy and the BAER was done afterwards, so it is a pretty accurate assessment of his sensory-neural hearing and he needs hearing aids."

Six weeks later, a tympanogram showed Reid's middle ears to be full again. The doctor insisted on ventilation tubes. Then in a short follow-up environmental hearing test, Reid's hearing was evaluated as age-appropriate. His hearing aids were taken away.

First I had been told that the Brain Stem Auditory Evoked Response test was supposed to be accurate, in spite of his middle ears. Now I was told that this BAER test was new and that the result was sometimes inaccurate. I did not know which was the more accurate test, the fancy one in an operating room with an anaesthetic or the VRA (Variable Response Audiometry) test we had seen. In the testing room there was a teddy bear behind a screen which lit up as a reward for looking in its direction when the baby heard a sound from that direction. Reid had already learned to visually sweep back and forth, no matter what else was going on. If he wanted to look at the bear, he looked at it whether lit or not. He occasionally located sounds to his left, never to his right. The audiologist told me I was hung up on the idea of hearing aids and hysterical. She reassured me Reid's age-appropriate hearing would develop as he grew. He was six months old.

The year Reid turned one, I was teaching recorder as a volunteer parent at school. Reid came along in his stroller and fell asleep, even though twenty-one shrill, obnoxious, screeching plastic recorders were being played. The noise was unbelievable, yet Reid fell asleep.

The ENT, (ear, nose and throat doctor) convinced he had cured Reid's hearing problems with tubes, insisted on regular tympanograms, but not hearing tests. He decided Reid was hyperactive. The tubes fell out regularly. The doctor would look into Reid's ear canals with an otoscope and declare, "This child's ears are perfect." I demanded hearing tests and was told there was no need to waste valuable time and equipment on Reid's perfect ears. Reid was fifteen months old. Finally, the doctor said we could have another hearing test when he would be eighteen months old, because a year would have passed since his last one.

We went back to our family doctor and insisted on another audiology clinic in another hospital. The doctor asked why Reid never had worn his hearing aids for his "well baby" checkup. I said, "The audiologist at the children's hospital took them back." The doctor commented that he had thought it rather strange that he never saw Reid wearing hearing aids, but had assumed that I could not be bothered using them in public.

My best friend is a psychologist. Together we watched the development of Reid very closely. One day she listened to his speech and concluded he did not have any, at eighteen months. I said to the doctor, "Marcia Swaby, BA, MS, the child's psychologist, says his speech is grossly deficient." The doctor perked right up, "A psychologist says the speech is grossly deficient?" This gave credence to my amateur knowledge.

At the end of it all, we got a referral to another audiology clinic. We had to wait three months. Reid was twenty-one months old when he had his second BAER on his left ear, which proved to have a mild/moderate loss, and twenty-three months old when he had his second BAER on his right ear which proved to have a severe/profound loss.

Actually, Reid's story is appalling. In the mid-1980's in a major medical center, it took twenty-one months to get hearing aids on a high-risk child who had hearing problems from birth, or very shortly thereafter and whose parents knew what was wrong. We should have had more confidence in ourselves, and not ever considered there was the slightest possibility that we were wrong. As the months passed, I did become difficult. Parents are usually right when they are talking about their own children.

When Reid was a newborn baby, my husband Ross was vice-president of a large advertising agency and commuted weekly between Montreal and Toronto. In Montreal he lived in a fancy hotel, where a maid left chocolates on his pillow every night. For several months he spent the weekends in culture shock as he returned home to four little children and a messy house. After the first week he learned to get his laundry done at the hotel. Eventually he changed jobs so he could live with his family.

Life in the advertising business has its ups and downs, but there is more freedom to come and go in that profession than is granted to many other people, countered, however, by many long nights. Ross came with me to all of Reid's hearing tests after it became obvious that people were not listening to me. The second audiologist was delighted to have both parents there and involved us in the process. Ross was watching the computer printout and knew Reid's level of hearing loss before I did. Neither of us grieved. The audiologist was prepared for emotional devastation and had tissues handy. Our immediate and joint response was, "What can we do to make this as good as possible?"

If one parent goes with the child for a hearing test and comes home with the results, that parent is immediately a gatekeeper for information. The other parent must ask, "What has happened, what does it mean, what can we do?" of a parent who might not understand enough to explain. A gatekeeper deals out information as he or she feels necessary, often withholding information in order to remain the gatekeeper. "Well, I guess he or she needs to know how to put the hearing aids in next week. This week it is my job because I know best." I think gatekeeping is destructive to a relationship because one parent must become a child while the other becomes the teacher. Parents are meant to have an adult-adult relationship all the time.

Ross relates to our children as 100 percent the parent with his choices. He gives me the same respect. I have usually been the one at home with the children, but my children have never heard, "Wait until Daddy gets home." I have too much respect for myself to do that. In some marriages one or the other spouse assumes all the responsibility for certain roles such as cooking, washing, or child rearing. When our oldest daughter was little we did it that way too but the process has evolved over the years to "Whoever is home is the homemaker, whoever is hungry is the cook" including the children.

To be Reid's parent required a whole new knowledge of parenting a child with hearing problems for each of us. I had more time to learn because I could take the children with me anywhere. Ross's boss had a fit when he turned up at work with them. We could not afford private professional help for the child, we could not delay through waiting lists for help, especially for speech therapy. We decided to become as good as we could on our own. I went to seminars, read most of the books, and became responsible for Reid's auditory input and environmental stimulation, but Ross and I talked every day. Talking over little problems really helps.

Many families find themselves moving in search of schooling, especially when the child is recently diagnosed and it seems to make sense to move into the backyard of the school for the Deaf. (This is a school where children of the Deaf culture are educated. There is no teaching of speech.) Some families split the parents and relocate the child with hearing problems with the parent who is going to be most involved. How can you talk to your spouse when separated by hundreds of miles?

After his retirement, Ross's father phoned more often than when he was working. Over the years I found out that this apparently tough businessman loved his son and grandchildren passionately. He was a practical sort who seldom appeared overwhelmed with emotion. One night he phoned me to say, "Thank you for sticking around and raising my grandchildren, particularly the last one. It was above the call of duty. My son chose well for his wife." Flabbergasted, I answered, "Thank you for raising my husband. I chose well too." In the harder times of a marriage, we have to remember we chose each other.

The fundamental strength of our relationship is the delicious gluttony of a huge bar of European chocolate, much too expensive to share with kids. Chocolate causes a euphoria yet leaves the brain unimpaired to deal with the little things there are to discuss. Ross and I stand shoulder-to-shoulder and face the days together. We talk, we are still best friends most of the time. We are separate, we are entwined. With four children, three dogs, and an old stone house responding to the laws of gravity, we always have something to talk about.

Figure 1.1. Looking at Reid in the hospital nursery.

Chapter 2
Grief: Oh God!
What Do We Do Now?

When the audiologist gives you the news that your child has a hearing problem, she has been trained to watch your reactions and to stop giving you information when you take the step across from questioning to realization of the diagnosis, and into the first stage of the grieving process.

Due to an odd quirk of timing, I was doing a seminar with Dr. D. Luterman, the world expert on grieving parents of children with hearing problems and thirty-six parents at a local school for the Deaf. I went from the audiologist and BAER (Brain Stem Auditory Evoked Response) testing back to the seminar and a supportive group of staff and parents. After a short description of the testing, Dr. Luterman asked if I was mad. I answered, "Yes, I am so angry that so many professionals were wrong, and did not listen to me, and as a result we have lost twenty-three months of his life when he could have been wearing hearing aids." So, there I was, a case study in grieving, by getting angry at all the people who had been wrong. My anger is there, even eight years later, because anyone who asks for a history of Reid's hearing problems gets five minutes of fact and ten minutes of diatribe. But it is getting better. It used to take much longer to vent my rage.

I have never cried because Reid has to wear hearing aids to hear properly. Those little plastic things on his ears give him the world. There is an undercurrent of stress relating to always doing the absolute best for the child. That is my way of telling the child that I am sorry.

Dr. Luterman said diagnosis changes nothing for the child, while the parent may be devastated. The child will get to know and love his hearing aids, and may either like or dislike them on the basis of what is in his ears or what he can now hear. The child has no concept of hearing problems. It has been a constant for him. It is the parent who must struggle to understand "hard of hearing," "hearing impaired," "profoundly deaf," "deaf," and "Deaf," what do they mean, and what is next?

Grieving makes other people uncomfortable. It helps to remember that for the professional, nothing has changed either. She may be supportive, or sympathetic, or informative, or withdrawing in the face of your grief. However, she is not going to take your child home for the night. You are. The most important thing you can do with the child is hug him, even if you are crying. Hug him and hug him some more. The child may be confused by the emotion he sees. He needs to know that he is good and loved, with or without hearing aids.

There are parents who have no idea that the child has a hearing problem before they get to the audiologist. Keith's parents found out that he was hard of hearing in the process of attempting to find out what might be normal about the child. The parents' grief could understandably be all encompassing for the child who was mildly retarded, with a cleft palate, and dwarfism, even before they got to the audiologist. At the hospital where he was born, the nurses had a terrible time relating to his mother when she sat with the baby and said, "Look, look at what I have produced!" Wrapped in bunting very carefully, it was possible to pretend the rest of him was normal, based on one little eye. The nurses wanted her to do that, so everyone would be comfortable. The mother had no intentions of any pretending for the nurses' comfort. She wanted to know everything she could possibly learn to make life better for her child. Making his life better began by looking at him, and perceiving him as still human, somehow, and going on from there. The mother had the most healthy attitude naturally. Most of the professionals the parents encountered suggested institutionalization. The parents' reaction was, "Well, put hearing aids on him, at least we can do that."

Support for parents at diagnosis is to get them to cooperate and to absorb as much information as they can, which usually has to do with the positive step of getting the hearing aids. The parents take the child home until the next appointment. The parents are expected to function as though nothing has happened and go on home. Hopefully the audiologist will give the parents a phone number where she can be reached to answer the questions the parents did not think of at the time.

When **both** parents are at the audiologist, at least one parent does not have the burden of telling the other parent the results of the test. While both may not react the same way to the diagnostics, at least the question of blaming the messenger for the bad news falls squarely on the audiologist's shoulders and not on one parent. Helping parents to handle their grief is a new facet of audiology, based on Kübler-Ross's work and the assumption that the parent or parents will start at some point in the cycle of shock, grief, anger, denial and acceptance, and will move through the cycle to a moment when they can begin to function again.

I believe that the fundamental grief reaction comes not from finding out that the baby or child is hard of hearing, but from voices in the mind screaming, "What do I do? What can I do?" and the terrible confusion of not knowing what to do about it. The best silencer for those voices and the answer to the questions is solid substantial information that something can be done. I think parents wander around telling everyone they know that the child has hearing problems in the hope that someone will have some information and will give it to them.

It is possible for the parents to be given information which they cannot comprehend, because they do not have degrees in aural habilitation. That inappropriate information will, by and large, be ignored, but even knowing that such information exists can be a steadying force. It is important not to get bogged down in too much conflicting information. It is always possible to simplify things so that everyone can understand: advertisers do it all the time. Parents need lots of appropriate information so that they can mull it over, talk about it, and try things on for size. The sooner the parents realize that several things can be done, the sooner they will get a handle on themselves and begin to explore. To sort out all the information with a steadying mentor would be ideal.

Joseph Conrad suggested that we tell stories we cannot comprehend, again and again until we have sufficiently understood what happened, can accept what happened and remember it, but go on with our lives. Certainly the first thing we do when we find out that our child has hearing problems is tell other people.

The other children in the family, if they are old enough to understand anything at all, have to be told the news. This can be as simple as, "Reid's ears don't work very well. We are getting him hearing aids to help," to a fairly complex explanation to a concerned older child. The siblings need to know the child is hard of hearing, but things can be done and they can help too. They may be concerned, especially children between six and ten years, that they are still full members of the family and will not lose out on too much of their own lives because a sibling has hearing problems. Children of this age are constantly dealing with the alternate forces of school, home and peer group, and do not always feel as secure as they might in one or another milieu. No matter what they say, they may be shaken to their toes to find out that a sibling has a problem. And even the most impartial of parents will have some life style changes to make, so, for a little while, the normal children may get less attention.

The parents may or may not react to the diagnosis of hearing problems with a desire to know, "**Why?**" According to Dr. James MacDougall at McGill University, in the United States, 66 percent of the parents have been given the etiology or cause for the condition, in Canada just under 50 percent know the cause.

Rubella (German Measles) during early pregnancy can cause a congenital hearing loss. Too much oxygen in intensive care and the baby might be blind. Not enough oxygen, as well as many drugs used in critical care for a newborn, can cause hearing problems. Meningitis and cytomegalovirus are viral infections which may leave the child with hearing problems. And there are good old-fashioned genetics. There are over two hundred causes of hearing problems, according to Dr. James MacDougall.

Not knowing why the child has hearing problems can lead to worrying. Eventually either you make up your mind by picking out the most likely circumstance from the pregnancy or the child's early life, telling it often enough that you come to believe it, or you decide there was no reason. Dealing with the **why** of a child's hearing problems can be spiritual. Some parents believe that God gave them a special child. At a **VOICE for Hearing-Impaired Children** (an oral parent advocacy group in Canada) parent night, Dr. Ken Moses explained his "raisin theory" suggesting that God threw a load of raisins over his shoulder, and where they landed the child had hearing problems. At a basic spiritual level where science does not yet attempt an explanation, we have to fill-in-the-blanks ourselves with whatever we can accept.

The **why** of hearing problems leads to, "What could I have done to prevent it?" This is the one that drives people crazy, because someone will always find a way of pinning guilt on to some previous action, such as taking aspirin for a headache. The parents of meningitis-related hearing loss drive themselves nuts with, "I should have taken the child to the doctor sooner." We do this, partly to give ourselves an understanding of the condition, but mostly because as humans we learn from experience. This is one mistake we do not want to make again. Even if the hearing problems are entirely related to something you did during pregnancy, you have to understand that what you **did** is not important. **What you are going to do from now on, in a positive scientific way, is what will help your child.**

> I've saved worshipping at the Shrine of Perpetual Guilt until last because mothers (who invented guilt) have devised more ways to punish themselves than any other species on the earth. They visit the shrine daily laying at its feet such wondrous questions as: How could I have permitted this to happen to my child? . . . I have no right to question God about how long I have to endure living like this . . . Forgive me. I locked the bathroom door again and pretended I wasn't there.
> **Erma Bombeck *I Want To Grow Hair* (1989)**

Telling the grandparents that a grandchild is hard of hearing can be tougher than finding out yourselves. They have high expectations of perfect grandchildren, having produced perfect children themselves. They do not spend as many hours with the child as the parents do, and those hours are spent with rose-tinted glasses. So it is very easy for grandparents to simply ignore your information and deny the hearing problems. On the other hand it is the grandparents to whom you first turn when you need help or understanding, and sometimes money, and it is quite natural to want them to know that the child is hard of hearing. Ross's Dad was sad when we told him that Reid was hard of hearing, but his first question was, "Do you need money for hearing aids?"

Granny denied the child's hearing problems. We argued, and explained, and showed her the hearing aids. It took some time for us to realize that it does not matter that she does not believe the child is hard of hearing. She can have any sort of a relationship with the child she wants, but if she does not speak clearly and at close range, he will not hear her. That is her problem, not Reid's or ours. A grandparent in denial can be a cause of never-ending anger to the parents who expected warmth, love and support. It gets even worse if the "handicapped" child gets picked on or shunned while the rest of the children are welcomed.

Your own siblings may react to the news with profound, sincere grief. My sister wept. Any reasonable sort of person has to say to themselves, "Thank God it wasn't my child." Then they immediately feel guilty and even worse than you do. Siblings and grandparents both need to know more than you might think they do. We did not go into great detail with anybody about Reid, because it is expensive phoning long distance, and there was no time or enough emotional stability for letters. My brother was a Special Education teacher for thirty years. I assumed he knew about children with hearing problems from his job. My siblings knew no more about hearing problems than we did before Reid came along.

Your best friends may be as devastated as you are by the diagnosis. Sometimes the stress is too much for the friendship, and you stop being good friends. Perhaps too, in this day of nuclear families who stay in touch with the rest of the family only on the telephone, we tend to rely on our friends where once there would have been family. Sometimes your friends are the best solace and source of information. They seldom are indifferent or don't care.

Many of our casual friends have assumed that Reid will not always have hearing problems and express surprise that he is still wearing hearing aids. Comments like that show that they are concerned but ignorant. In general, people are trying to help, not hurt you. This is also true about alternate philosophies, technologies, and miracle workers anywhere in the world, about which I found people telling us with great emphasis.

When you lose a child, eventually the grief cycle is passed through and the death becomes a very strong, sad memory. Death is final. Life goes on and your life goes on. When a child is diagnosed as handicapped in some way, that diagnosis will be there, barring miracles, for the rest of your life. You may forget that the child is hard of hearing in the day-to-day passing of life, but will be constantly reminded of the reality when the child has difficulty doing something. A hearing problem becomes a constant, but it does not become a memory. It is hard to expiate your grief because the child is alive and kicking and growing. Each new stage of childhood involves concessions to the condition and may set you off on the grieving routine at an entirely new level.

I have a prelingually hard-of-hearing child. This means his hearing was damaged before he learned how to talk. The memories of Reid's loud screeching before he started wearing hearing aids at age two are unforgettable. So while we have had to work very hard to bring his speech skills to life, the job of every parent of a prelingual hard-of-hearing child, we can only begin to empathize with the parent of a postlingually deafened child. It must be heart rending to have the memory of the child hearing and speaking normally before the event that caused the problems.

The parents of a postlingually hard-of-hearing child are reminded of the changes in their lives every time they forget, and call the child from another room. What was once so normal now is impossible. It is truly training by fire to be reminded that the child can no longer hear by these simple things we do as parents. The sooner that you think all these things through and train yourselves to live within the hearing aids' limitations, the easier your life can become again.

The technology of hearing aids has soared in the past ten years. We must be wary of other people saying, "I hated my aids when I was a child." Reid's new hearing aids, fine-tuned with in-the-ear microphone testing are almost as much of an improvement as the CD player is to the monaural record player. So even if you are repelled by the idea of the child wearing these things, you have to learn about them, so that you will understand what they can do. To me, hearing aid technology, properly utilized, is the scientific realization of miracles in the 1990's.

Ross and I both felt very positive about hearing aids right from the beginning, but even so we had problems putting the earmolds into the baby's ears. It takes a while to get good enough at the angles so insertion is a breeze. As the number of times we put in the aids rose to the thousands, we became as good as the hearing aid dealer. We stopped worrying that we were going to hurt the child's ears.

One of my children was taking music lessons when Reid was a baby. The mothers ended up with a sew-and-blow session in a waiting room. One day a mother came in, red-eyed and carrying a hankie. We inquired what was wrong. Finally she managed, "Georgie has to get glasses. I waited so long for this baby, he's the only one, and he will always need glasses, just like me." One of the other mothers said to her, "Pooh, what are glasses, practically everyone has them. Now look at this mother and child, pointing at Reid and me, "He's deaf and has hearing aids." Well, that poor mother just about died and turned to me with, "Hearing aids on a baby. Oh God, how can you just stand there? Hearing aids. . . . I am so sorry." I said to her, "You know, Reid can hear with hearing aids on." "Oh." she mumbled. I continued, "George can see better with his glasses than without them, can"t he?" "Yes." she admitted. I told her, "I think it is great that you watched for bad eyes and got George glasses now. Imagine if you had waited until he was in school." Well, I probably only made her feel 10 percent better, but 10 percent a day is 100 percent at the end of ten days.

The only time I resent the aids is when they fall off when Reid is playing or carrying on, and he unconsciously checks them by running one finger over each ear. I get a lump in my throat when he falls down, hurts and settles himself, but the aids are still hanging askew. He does not need any more indignity than that which comes with tripping or having a temper tantrum.

Sometimes your spouse grieves with you, sometimes he or she packs a bag and leaves. Traditionally fathers tended to deny hearing problems more than mothers, perhaps because the fathers went to work and the mothers went to the audiologist. It was quite easy for the fathers to just deny everything. Now fathers are in the delivery room, and they should be in the audiological testing rooms too, especially if both parents work. It is all right for your siblings or the grandparents to deny the child's hearing problems as long as they have no responsibility for the child. Prime caregivers such as fathers, mothers, teachers and babysitters must accept the child's hearing problems, or it is not safe for the child to be with them. It is possible to change schools, and babysitters, but really inconvenient to change spouses.

The child needs loving parents who are going to accept the reality of a child with hearing problems and do their best to deal with it. The reality may be somewhat less, but with good information and a little experience, it is easier to cope, on a day-to-day basis, than you ever thought it could be when you are first told, "Your child needs hearing aids to help him hear."

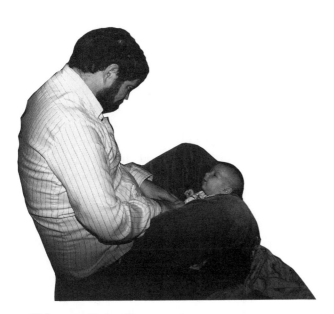

Chapter 3
It's Not Fair!

You will spend a lot of money on batteries, hearing aids, and repairs over the twenty years that you will parent your child. You will spend more money on transportation to take the child to the ear, nose and throat specialist, the speech clinician, the hearing aid dealer, the auditory-verbal therapist. You will probably never get the Louis Vuitton luggage. You might have to spend far more time looking than buying. It is not fair that you have to constantly battle your desires against specific needs for a handicapped child. Other children in the family will resent wearing old shoes longer while the money goes for new earmolds. Usually Mom wears the old shoes, because her feet have stopped growing and nobody can see your soles when you stand up.

Before Reid, I tried to be scrupulously impartial with all our children. If one child got a new T-shirt, three children got new T-shirts, little cars, lollipops, all the token "I Love You's" we buy, were always evaluated for fairness. Usually two children were happy and one was hard done by, even if we had three identical toys. I learned I could turn myself inside out being fair and someone would be unhappy. So I decided to be deliberately unfair.

When a child needs something, only that child goes with me. Greatly enjoying each other's company, we have lunch together, take care of the 'must-do' whether it is new earmolds or shoes, and cruise around for the wants. Without three other children chorusing "Buy me . . ." "I need" . . . I stay calmer and nicer too. We evaluate price and determine desire, usually by how much the child is willing to contribute his own money which he has earned or been given by Grandpa. If we can only "look" at the "wants," the child must understand that too. A child's passion for something like a Batman T-shirt usually ends when he gets it, wears it once and drops it under the bed.

Tiffany, our oldest child has always appeared to be positive towards her youngest brother. She nearly always does more than her share to help around the house, do well at school, and have a good life. The second child Barbara, between the ages of seven and ten, was the only child to attack Reid through his hearing aids, either by shouting at him, or making snide remarks, or putting her hands over his hearing aids to cause feedback. She would go outside the family and tell people that she was treated unfairly because she had a hard-of-hearing brother. As Barbara is growing older she is becoming more interested in helping her brother, rather than competing with him. There is an amazing intensity in her ability to love and help Reid, even while playing "school" or "house."

My first son has an altruistic soul. William was awarded a pumpkin at school for good behavior. While talking to a pretty little girl, he found out that she did not have a pumpkin, so he gave her his. William did not tell us about the reward, but the Principal began a chat with "That is some special child you have there . . ." He is.

William and Reid share a bedroom, which William regards as his own special torture for unknown past sins. Reid is happy to have protection and fellowship with his idolized older brother. William sees the four years difference in age, Reid does not. Within the family they fight, argue, tussle and snap at each other. Outside the family, William bears a heavy responsibility to protect his brother. We make sure that William does not always have Reid in tow.

William is equipped with powerful lungs and a naturally loud voice. Even when Reid was unaided, he could usually hear William speak when they played and part of Reid's idolatry of William is a result of being able to hear him when other people moved their mouths, but made no sounds. If Reid would just stay out of William's possessions and not always hang around when William has friends over they would have a great relationship. Even so, within their relationship there is no consideration of Reid's hearing problems and they are best buddies a surprising amount of time.

Reid has three siblings with three very different philosophies of life. Only one child stooped to attack her brother on the basis of his disability and hearing aids. I did what I could to protect Reid from such willful behavior, but it is a kind of training for coping with the real world.

Siblings of children with hearing problems, in formal encounter groups will often bring up the "duty" which they feel toward their hard-of-hearing sibling. They might never admit it to their parents, for fear of the lectures they would get about fairness, but they **do** feel that it is not fair that the hard-of-hearing child seems to get more love, attention or rewards from the whole family. Reid is rewarded with a small toy every time he has to go for a hearing test, or repairs to the hearing aids, or new earmolds. Over the years this has amounted to a significant pile of toys. All of my children have commented that Reid is spoiled and gets away with things that they would never have been allowed to do, a fair comment. I hope that it is at least partly because he is the youngest child and not just because he is hard of hearing.

I believe Reid has the right to say "It's not fair," but that must be tempered with thankfulness for the technology and knowledge which we have today. Reid can wish for normal hearing, I can wish for normal hearing for him, but he must understand that we have provided the best technology available to compensate him for his less-than-perfect inner ears.

I have often seen physically challenged children wearing clothing which is too big. It looks as though the child is slightly less than loved, although it may only be for ease of dressing. From the day that Reid put on hearing aids, his hair has been kept trimmed, his clothing the right size and trendy, his footwear reasonably new. Because he is hard of hearing I pay special attention to his appearance, more than for the other children. We do not have enough money to dress all the children for peer group approval (teacher approval too), but I feel it is very important for Reid to make a first impression of good grooming.

A young child probably does not think much about his ears or hearing aids. Either they are there, or they are not. Either they work well, or they malfunction and cause him distress. Even at age five, Reid walked around with a non-functioning hearing aid without seeming to notice. Perhaps he just liked not having to hear. Perhaps he was unaware that he was not hearing.

At almost five, Reid still did not know he was hard of hearing, or what a hearing problem was. I found it easier to explain blindness than deafness to him. I wanted him to label himself without much consideration of his ears, bionic or natural. He came home from day camp saying "I'm deaf." Isn't it wonderful, what children learn when they leave home. I said, "Your name is Reid. You're not deaf, you're Reid." I have taught him to respond to labelling by others by introducing himself, and to try a little humor when possible.

The issues of rejecting hearing aids because they conflict with self-image are more important when the child is older. The young child wears them because the parents show that he must. At any point in Reid's life he will always have the right to say, "It's not fair" and he is absolutely right, but he must also understand that we have done our best to help him. While it is not fair that he has to live with hearing problems and hearing aids, that's the way it is.

Chapter 4
Hard of Hearing Forever

Some people might equate hearing aids with the bionic gimmicks that television characters have for arms and legs. The truth is not so great. Children wearing prosthetics are better off with them, but an artificial leg is not a real leg, a hook is not a hand. Hearing aids help, but they do not cure hearing problems. In order to hear, the child or adult must put in his hearing aids and work hard to listen.

We want our children to be like ourselves. We have high expectations of how hard we are willing to work and almost deny a normal childhood to these children in the intense efforts of learning to listen. As each generation of parents has had access to better technology and teaching methods for their hard-of-hearing child, the goal of more participation in an active, normal hearing life seems more attainable.

Our friend Peter has a mid-life progressive hearing loss, currently at a moderate level and wears in-the-ear aids. My husband, Ross, fractured his skull and has no hearing in one ear, I have a mild loss. Only Sally has a normal set of ears. When we play bridge, the background noise is kept to a minimum, the hearing environment is at a maximum. Sally usually hears the bidding, the rest of us have our own ideas of what was said. Peter does not think of himself as a hard-of-hearing person. He expects no consideration of his hearing aids in his work situation, or socially. He's a quiet guy most of the time, but becomes lively when conversation is comfortably within earshot and he is not struggling with distance, as well as hearing loss.

Another friend, Lars is forty years old, has children and a spouse. Lars has a severe loss, is unable to use a telephone, or understand any speech without speechreading. His mother, Inger Lise, was told, when he was diagnosed in the 1950's, to have his tonsils out and send him to a school for the Deaf where he could learn to sign. His mother, had two other children before him, and six more after him, and was coping with English as a second language herself. She told the doctors, "Over my dead body. He will learn to speak just like the rest of the world." By herself, with no guidance, she taught Lars to speak. The first time we met, Lars said, "My Mother taught me how to speak." Reid saw his behind-the-ear (BTE) aids and said, "Mummy, that man has hearing aids." At the same time, Lars was saying to Inger Lise, "Mom, that kid has hearing aids." Lars then said to me, "I had a box aid when I was a child. I hated it. But I have just got new aids and they are so much better than even the last pair were."

Lars kindly answered some questions for me:
PAM: Can you define yourself?
LARS: I am a handicapped individual.

PAM: Have you ever felt any pull to the Deaf community? (where those who have hearing impairments do not talk nor listen nor speechread, and communicate only by sign language, and 'Deaf' is capitalized like a nationality, 'French,' or 'Spanish.')

LARS: The only time I ever felt any pull to the Deaf community was when I lost a hearing aid recently. I felt suicidal. I felt that I should have grown up in a Deaf community because then I would be with true peers, i.e. someone equal to me, someone who would understand.

PAM: Did you have any Deaf friends as a child?
LARS: I had no Deaf friends as a child.

PAM: Do you have any Deaf friends as an adult?
LARS: I have no Deaf friends as an adult.

PAM: Do you have advantages from being hard of hearing?
LARS: There are many, and if I sought sympathy I would never find them. For example: TV.—I hate movies, they are so hard to figure out, but I can figure out a movie with no sound, it's like putting two and two together. (Lars did not have a closed caption decoder.) I can figure people out too, however there is a fine line between imagination and reality. Of course shutting off noises and quiet sleep is an advantage.

PAM: Do you like your hearing aids?
LARS: No, I hate them.

PAM: Are your hearing aids part of you or something you put on?
LARS: My hearing aids are both a part of me and something I put on.

PAM: Did you feel discriminated against as a child?
LARS: Yes.

PAM: Do you feel discriminated against as an adult?
LARS: Yes.

PAM: Do you lipread?
LARS: Yes.

PAM: Can you use a telephone?
LARS: No. I can't understand it i.e. **bee, lee, tea, see, sea.**

PAM: What is the biggest problem with hearing aids today?
LARS: People think you are fine. Is a lame man fine with a prosthetic leg?

PAM: What was your biggest problem as a child?
LARS: My biggest problem as a child was being treated like a "retarded child."

PAM: Did you expect special consideration because of your hearing problems?

LARS: I was showered with special consideration as a child, only by adults, and I hated it.

PAM: If you had a deaf child, what would you do that was not done for you?
LARS: If I had a deaf child, he would automatically have what I didn't have, **a deaf parent.**

PAM: What would you like to say to parents and children with hearing problems of today?
LARS: Most people think handicapped people need sympathy or want it. That is a weakness. I am strong. The weak fall prey to the wolves.

PAM: Who was the most influential adult in your learning to talk?
Lars: My mother.

Lars' childhood was encumbered by a big, ugly hearing aid and even more by ugly children for friends. His answers to me reflect a basic honesty for which I am grateful. I had been running down the garden path with Reid, thinking he would be a hearing person when he grows up. Reid will be able to function in the hearing world, but he will always be hard of hearing.

This quotation helped Lars as a teenager:

> DESIDERATA
> Go placidly amid the noise and remember what peace there may be in silence. As far as possible without surrender, be on good terms with all persons . . . Beyond a Wholesome discipline, be gentle with yourself. You are a child of the universe, no less than the trees and the stars; you have a right to be here. And whether or not it is clear to you, no doubt the universe is unfolding as it should.
> **Found in Old St.Paul's Church, Baltimore, Maryland dated 1692.**

Lars' wife, Bonnie, also answered some questions which show the extent to which Lars is integrated into the hearing world. Here is what Bonnie said:

PAM: Is Lars a deaf person or person who is deaf?
BONNIE: A person who is deaf.

PAM: What concessions do you have to make in your relationship because of his hearing problems?
BONNIE: Not many. Making phone calls for him is hardly a big deal.

PAM: Would your life be any different if he had better hearing?
BONNIE: Not that I can imagine.

PAM: Did you notice he was cute or hard of hearing first?
BONNIE: Cute, of course.

PAM: Did you know anything about hearing problems before Lars?
BONNIE: No.

PAM: Are you aware of his hearing aids when all is well?
BONNIE: I don't think about his hearing problems unless his aids are
feeding back.

PAM: Do you ever give up in a discussion because he's having trouble
understanding?
BONNIE: Only if there are a lot of people around, or in the middle of
a movie, I'll put off explaining until the time is right. Other than that,
I'm so in tune with him, we seldom have problems that way.

Spouses, or future spouses are very important people because they have
a choice, "Do I want to live with this person forever?" Parents do not
have this choice. In a parent sharing session, a parent of a hard-of-
hearing teenager commented, "It would be handy if my son would marry
an audiologist who would have a basic professional knowledge of the
challenges the hard-of-hearing person faces." Bonnie is not an audiologist. She lives with Lars as he is, repeats patiently when he has not
heard well and makes his phone calls. One day when Bonnie was not
home, the phone rang. Lars picked up the phone and announced, "I
am deaf and cannot hear on the phone. Please call later when my wife
will be home." then hung up. Again and again the phone rang, finally
he said, "Look, are you stupid or something? I cannot hear on the
phone. Call back later." Lars' mother, Inger Lise called back later.

Inger Lise's previous experience with Lars gave her more patience with
Reid than most people had. We even celebrated Reid's fifth birthday

with a party at her house and a magnificent cake decorated with little wooden chickens, Danish, and Canadian flags and candles.

Inger Lise repeatedly told me, "Reid will learn to talk. You will find it within yourself to help him." I was lucky to have Inger Lise as a good friend. Perhaps it is her quality of "Tz'u" or caring and compassion for other people. Tz'u is one of the tenets of Taoism, which is based on the character for heart. Tz'u gives us courage to rise to the situation, even if we are not clever or scholarly and from Tz'u comes wisdom.

Lars and Inger Lise have a close, comfortable relationship. Lars frequently brings up the fact that his mother taught him to speak and that he is grateful to her. Children usually do not appreciate their parents' efforts until it is too late to say "thank you" to their parents for the fact that they could speak. Perhaps they forget the hours and hours of work that the parents did, for the children's language, when they might have been reading a book, being lovers or having a nap. Lars, of course, is past the glittery stage of youth (Sorry, Lars, but I am too) and is very aware that there was not one other person in the world who would have taken the time out of her own life to teach him to talk, except his mother. It is beautiful when he thanks her.

When we look at our children and evaluate their futures, we must remember it is a future filled with hope. While it seems that we are poised on the pinnacle of technology, we are only part way up. Digital aids are in their infancy as a viable product. I dream of a day when hearing aids will be invisible and work regardless of distance or background noise.

There are dreamers in every field, whose abilities to discern a problem and extrapolate a solution carry mankind forward to technological brilliance that had been thought impossible by the more pedestrian plodders just a few years earlier. Although, historically we have to learn that our children will always be hard of hearing and have to make concessions to the state of the art today. We do not have even a glimmer of what is to come, just as the Beatles never dreamed of the compact disc player when they created "Abbey Road."

Chapter 5
A Whole New Crowd of Friends

The diagnosis, evaluation, and analysis of hearing problems involves meeting a whole new crowd of people. If a parent suspects any kind of limiting condition in a child, the parent will want to question the professional for guidelines, observe the child, and write it all down, preferably with dates and age references. Comments made by teachers or friends supporting the parent's observations are valid. Our family doctor finally changed the referral for Reid to go to back to the first audiology clinic because of an informal assessment of Reid's speech by my friend, a child psychologist.

Doctors

Many people are intimidated by doctors. They feel intimidated by them because they look busy and sound breathless all the time. People also feel stupid when they don't understand what a doctor's talking about the first time around, so they don't ask again. And let's be honest here, people. English is not a doctor's first language.
Erma Bombeck, *I Want to Grow Hair, I Want to Grow Up,*
I Want to Go to Boise. **(1989)**

The family doctor should refer you to an otolaryngologist or ear, nose and throat (ENT) specialist. The ENT will determine the nature of the hearing problems, whether a child has a conductive loss, (the result of middle ear problems), or sensorineural loss (stemming from inner ear or auditory nerve problems) or both. The ENT, otologist or otolaryngologist should suggest that your next step should be to see an audiologist. If not, you can find an audiologist on your own.

Children with mild losses may never get beyond the ENT to an audiologist. These children can cope with and cover their hearing problems well, yet may do poorly in school, especially in subjects which require listening skills. This is now recognized as the minimal auditory deficiency syndrome. The effort to develop listening and hearing in a systematic and sustained manner requires the support of specialists. Dr.Richard Seewald, of the University of Western Ontario, has said the limit of normal hearing for a child with a prelingual hearing loss should be set at 15 dB. A child should have normal hearing available to him. A child's degree of normal hearing, however much it is diminished by a hearing loss, should be recognized and developed to the fullest.

Audiologists

The ENT should refer you to an audiologist if the child's hearing loss is greater than 15 dB, or you can find one on your own. Of all the people the parents of a child with hearing problems must consult, the audiologist is the most important. The findings of the audiologist help to determine what kind of assistance the child is going to get, based on testing and observation. She determines the threshold of hearing in each ear, and analyzes the usefulness of the residual hearing. She has detailed knowledge of hearing aids on the market, which must be constantly updated, and selects earmolds and hearing aids which are appropriate for each child.

An audiologist's training takes many years and continues after graduation. Certification and institutional accreditation maintain standards for the professional. In the United States, audiologists are certified by the **American Speech-Language-Hearing Association**. Ideally, your audiologist should be experienced with children, and have recently attended a refresher course at a major teaching center.

At the end of the testing, the audiologist will review the results with you. She should give you a piece of paper with the child's audiogram on it, (See Chapter 6) and her recommendations for hearing aids and earmolds. If she does not give you a copy of the audiogram, ask for it. You must learn the implications of the child's aided thresholds. You might not be able to remember by the time you get home. Write it down then and there. Ask as many questions as you can.

The audiologist should make an immediate referral to a speech pathologist, as part of the diagnostic follow up. Toronto's Hospital for Sick Children following a diagnosis of hearing loss offers a complete assessment of the child which includes speech pathology, neurology, psychology, cardiology (hearing problems and cardiac defects sometimes go hand in hand,) and social work. From a medical viewpoint, this is a fabulous program which should be emulated throughout the world. The parents call it "five days of hell."

Hearing Aid Dealers

"Hi. Big guy!" Knowing how to approach children successfully is as important for the hearing aid dealer as it is essential for the doctor, the audiologist, the speech pathologist and all the professionals involved with the child. Taking five minutes to make friends with a child can make such a difference in a parent's life. Our dealer talks with Reid so he goes along with him. After the appointment Reid gets a soft drink. Reid is allowed to decide which chair he will sit in. It is clever to allow the child some element of control so that he feels less intimidated. It has taken me four years to find a hearing aid dealer with the particular caring and competence of our dealer. If you do not land on your feet first try, do not be afraid to shop around.

The audiologist may refer you to a particular hearing aid dealer but you can go to any hearing aid dealer you choose. Ideally the dealer should be in your community. You will be taking the child to the hearing aid dealer many times for new earmolds and for repairing of broken hearing aids. With so many visits involved, the dealer must be good with your child.

Speech Pathologists/Therapists/Clinicians

A speech pathologist goes to university for five to seven years, and many have two-to-three-year master degrees, as well. She studies the problems involved with human speech and language and the methods used in therapy to fix what is wrong. She also learns some psychology and audiology. In the United States, speech clinicians or therapists work in public schools. In Canada, speech pathologists are usually found in hospitals or in schools. There are a few speech pathologists in private practice.

A pathologist is a person who examines the evidence and makes a diagnosis. A therapist is a person who provides exercises to improve what the pathologist has found. A speech pathologist assesses the child's speech and language and determines the errors the child is producing, while considering the child's age and where he ought to be on the developmental ladder. Her office usually has a good tape recorder to take a sample of the child's language while he plays with toys selected to evoke the vocabulary she wants to listen to. Somewhere there is usually a large mirror and hidden in a drawer will be a candle, tissues, and a feather and possibly a tongue depressor and a flashlight.

Speech pathologists have a selection of standardized testing books written by experts such as the *Goldman Fristoe Test of Articulation*, the *Fisher-Logemann Test of Articulation Competence*, the *Sequenced Inventory of Communication Development, Preschool Language Scale*, the *Test of Auditory Comprehension of Language (Revised)*. The testing 'books' have pictures of line drawings of objects and actions which the child will either have to identify to test vocabulary and pronunciation or articulation, or listen to the pathologist describe them, and try to say the words or identify the concept.

Once the pathologist has identified the speech problems presented by the child, then therapy can begin. While speech pathologists are inspired by what they can do for a child, they need parental support which begins with getting the child there on time, every time, and ends with the parent carrying out the suggestions of the speech pathologist at home, around the clock.

The teaching of speech and language can be different for a child with hearing problems simply because the child cannot hear some sounds. So, when there are no available services, either you must find a speech pathologist with an interest or previous experience with hard-of-hearing children, or failing that you must convince your speech pathologist and her hospital to send her to attend a specialized course to learn the basics of the trade. Or you can go to the course yourself and take on the job of teaching speech and language while relying on the speech pathologist to do regular assessments of the child's progress, which is what we did.

When dealing with programs and schools which have on-staff speech services, one needs to determine the background and experience through appropriate means. Then work step-by-step with the institution to constructively remedy deficiencies.

Interview with Gay Gretton, Speech Pathologist:

PAM: What do you expect the parent to do?
GRETTON: During the preschool years, someone who spends time with the child should attend sessions and participate in therapy. Home programming should be clear with one to two attainable goals set. The therapist should be available by telephone anytime. The therapist plants the seed, but the parent waters it. Parent workshops are ideal for acquiring basic information and for sharing. Workshops should consist of parents with similar needs.

PAM: Do you understand when parents become overwhelmed with their responsibilities?
GRETTON: When adequate support (emotional, physical . . .) is not available, and expectations are high, exhaustion or burnout can occur. Often, feelings of guilt, anger, grief, ("Is there some way in which I am responsible for my child's speech and language/hearing problems?" or "Why me?"), need to be dealt with.

PAM: How do you handle lack of progress or long plateaus?
GRETTON: Lack of progress may be a result of one or more conditions:

- Inappropriate goals, lack of identification of the steps required to reach the goals.
- Child/parent/therapist burnout, meaning time for a change.
- The child may be progressing in another area. Keep in mind the whole person, e.g. he has mastered a complicated physical activity, and lacks energy to work on another.

- Sometimes one is "knocking one's head against a brick wall" without much progress despite appropriate and endless stimulation.
- Is the child ready? Suddenly the child masters a skill, while he may have been accumulating the knowledge, integrating, comparing and waiting to achieve a certain level of competence before exposing him/herself.

PAM: At what point do you refer a hard-of-hearing child to someone with more specialized knowledge?
GRETTON: As early as possible. Or the speech language pathologist may educate herself by reading, research, phone contacts, and workshops.

PAM: When the child is badly behaved, do you blame the parents and do you expect the parents to mediate?
GRETTON: Since becoming the mother of two boys, I have gone through a dramatic transition in my opinions regarding parents and parenting. Children behave inappropriately for countless reasons, what they may be telling us is:

- I have to go to the bathroom. It's nap time.
- I'm nervous because you have put me in a strange room and you want me to do something that I find hard to do.
- I'm not stupid. I do not know what you are asking, so I will take you off track by misbehaving.
- I ate umpteen sweet snacks when Mummy was not looking.
- My Mom does not really want to be here, neither do I!
- I want to see what I can get away with before Mom/the speech person stops me. I wonder what they will do.
- I have a middle ear infection that is driving me crazy.

Thanks, Gay.

Auditory-Verbal Therapists

The auditory-verbal therapist reviews audiological work-ups, tests occasionally to monitor progress in listening, comprehension, vocabulary, expressive language, receptive language, and provides therapy as needed. While a speech pathologist might be a little hazy on the frequency of a speech sound, the auditory-verbal therapist knows exactly what it is, in all formants, and whether the child can or cannot hear the sound. The auditory-verbal therapist will develop and provide a program for your child based on his level of hearing loss and his stage of development.

Dr. Ling provides a good overview of each of the auditory-verbal methods in his book, *Early Intervention for Hearing-Impaired Children: Oral Options. (1984)* The International Committee on Auditory-Verbal Communication (ICAVC), a special committee of the Alexander Graham Bell Association for the Deaf, was formed in 1979 by Helen Beebe, Daniel Ling, Doreen Pollack, and many others. They agreed to call these methods the Auditory-Verbal Approach. In 1986 when ICAVC decided to be independent from the Alexander Graham Bell Association, Auditory-Verbal International (AVI) was formed.

Today, in the auditory-verbal approach, listening is integrated into the total personality of a child who is hard of hearing. Learning to listen is highlighted by sitting beside a child, or having him sit on your lap. Speechreading is only discouraged during therapy sessions for those who tend to rely on it.

To find out about auditory-verbal programs where you live, contact:

Auditory-Verbal International
2121 Eisenhower Avenue,Suite 402
Alexandria, Virginia 22314
U.S.A.

Judy Simser
Superintendant-Aural Habilitation,
Children's Hospital of Eastern Ontario
401 Smyth Road, Ottawa, Ontario, K1H 8L1
CANADA

Parent-Therapist Relationships

It is better to see an auditory-verbal therapist once a month than not at all. Reid visited **VOICE for Hearing-Impaired Children's** auditory-verbal therapist, once a month from age two-and-a-half to almost five. For Reid, it was a long drive, a time to sit still during therapy, and lunch before the drive home. It was my impetus to keep going, and to learn as much as I could.

Our therapist was particularly good at suggesting, rather than directing. She never made us feel that we had failed, although occasionally we were praised lavishly for a few things which had not been as tough to do as the things with which we were experiencing difficulty. This kept our chins up.

My child's learning to listen campaign was aided by lots of hearing, and we were rewarded with many successes. Reid had great difficulty realizing that speech is a mode of communication. There were times when I could not work, or Reid paused endlessly at one level. **At no point would I ever say, "We are failing and must give up." Failure just means postponing this week's goal to next week.**

The relationship between parent and therapist is fragile because the parent does not know as much as the therapist does, but the parent knows considerably more than the average person does and **much more about that particular child**! There is nothing the matter with intelligent questioning of the reasons why the therapist is doing a certain thing a certain way, such as seating the child so he is unable to speechread during the session. It is not what the therapist does in the course of a one hour lesson that affects the child, **but what you do the rest of the time**.

School System People

Even if the child is not anywhere near school age, contact your school system's central office. Our school board has a special education officer for hard-of-hearing children. Every time the child has an assessment done, send a copy to the board officer. She will open a file and by the time the child is ready for school, the board will have a complete file of all testing done.

In Ontario, a province in Canada, children with various problems may be identified to the school authorities through a formal procedure called an IPRC (Identification, Placement and Review Committee). It has been my experience that the IPRC allows a variety of services to be provided for the child, but you have to know what the child's needs are going to be next year. The board officer becomes an advocate for your child within the school system and can represent the child's needs when you are not there yourself. She also knows who is doing what within the resources of your community, or school system.

In the United States the education system must provide the most appropriate education for a child under IDEA (Individuals with Disabilities Education Act) which was formerly known as PL 94-142.

Educational Audiologists

I asked Riza Razack, an educational audiologist, and a parent of a hard-of-hearing child to describe the role of an educational audiologist. This is what he told me:

PAM: What does an educational audiologist do?
RAZACK: We look at the whole child, and determine his skills through testing and observation, both individually and in the classroom. We want to see our recommendations used in the classroom, the community and the child's home. We educate teachers, parents, and the community through training sessions, seminars and meetings to increase understanding of the hard-of-hearing child's talents and needs. We are part of the team and reinforce our role through communication with others concerned with the child.

I want to emphasize the philosophical difference between an **educational** audiologist and a **clinical** audiologist. A **clinical** audiologist approaches a child with a hearing loss from a medical model where there is a problem, which has to be determined and dealt with, either through the use of hearing aids or preferential seating in the class. The diagnosis is in terms of "hearing loss." An **educational** audiologist looks at what the child can hear, using all technologies available. It is a very positive outlook.

PAM: Your services sound quite fabulous. Are they limited to children with severe or profound losses?

RAZACK: **Children with mild losses have needs too**. We are dealing with the abilities of the child and not a charted line or threshold determined by some political or medical protocol.

Thank you, Mr. Razack.

Reid came with me to the school where Mr. Razack has his office. I suggested, "Look carefully at the children's ears." His eyes got very big as he commented, "Mummy, Lots of these kids have hearing aids, just like me." It was exciting to see other children wearing hearing aids and going to school. He could hardly wait to tell his family he had seen children, **"Just like me!"**

Itinerant Preschool Teachers of the Deaf

Some school systems employ an itinerant preschool teacher of the deaf whose job is to educate the parent about hearing problems, hearing aids, teaching techniques, alerting to sound, play audiometry, and to get the child started in either an oral or sign program. The teacher works with the child for as long as the child can be sweetly persuaded to cooperate. Then the teacher turns her attention to the parents with suggestions to make life easier, and techniques to promote the development of speech and language. She has been trained to help the parents move through the cycle of grief, anger, denial and confusion following diagnosis.

The teacher comes with toys to develop certain skills, with books which will be left with you until the next visit and with lesson plans and sheets of information. But more importantly, as with the best teachers, and as it happened to us, the teacher comes with a completely cheerful attitude about your child and his special set of problems. She can be spiritually uplifting when everything else seems bleak and pointless. Be friends, be there when she arrives and use what you can to augment your auditory-verbal program. Both of my itinerant preschool teachers were wonderful, warm, caring individuals. Their knowledge helped when we knew so little.

Interview with Itinerant Preschool Teacher

PAM: How long have you been an itinerant preschool teacher?
TEACHER: Fifteen years.

PAM: What made you become an itinerant teacher?
TEACHER: Little kids have always been special for me, and hard-of-hearing children need my help to get a better start.

PAM: What do you think about while you travel from place to place?
TEACHER: Probably the toughest thing about my job is the variety of students and parents, each of whom must have my best. If the morning session has been with a parent using an oral approach and it is time for the parent to consider sign language, that parent is dealing with a tremendous sense of failing. I feel the parent's anger with other methods for not having worked and with me for saying so. This is an emotional morning. I have to present a fresh face after lunch, at the home of an avid oral parent who is meeting with success. She feels isolated in parenting and probes around to find out what other parents are doing.

PAM: What do you do when the child is not prepared to work?
TEACHER: I come to play with the child, and do things like decorating ice cream cones with icing to make Christmas trees. The children like that and have positive memories for the next time I come. The parent can watch, or participate and carry over ideas for herself. When the child has had enough, he can go play by himself, or sleep while I talk to the parent.

PAM: How about when the child is a rank little rotter? Do you feel the parent should control the child?
TEACHER: Most children are not rank little rotters unless they are tired, hungry, or getting sick. I try to look at all the variables. A parent stuck with a little rotter desperately needs some support. I try to provide that. My job is not a job for people who do not like children, in all their manners and moods. I think, though, that the parents make a bigger deal about the child's misbehavior than I do.

Thanks, "Whiz." {Reid called his teacher "Ma teacha Whiz."}

Looking to the Future: Kindergarten Teachers

Traditionally very little has been done for children with mild or moderate hearing losses including the accurate collecting of statistics. Based on my children's friends, there is at least one child per class with chronic middle ear problems, or a slightly louder voice which might denote a hearing loss. Carol Flexer suggests a population of eight million children with hearing difficulties in America. Teachers usually have not been taught special techniques for children with hearing problems in their classrooms. A regular classroom teacher probably will not know anything more about hard-of-hearing children than you did before you had one.

Teachers cannot be assessed as good with children with hearing problems until they have had one in their class, met the challenge and successfully passed the child on to the next level. It will usually be on the basis of how your child progresses that a teacher acquires a reputation and so do you.

If the child benefits from an assistive listening device (ALD), used either alone, or coupled to his personal hearing aid, the classroom teacher needs information on how it is used. In most cases it is a frequency modulation (FM) unit worn by the child while the teacher wears a microphone. The teacher must understand that the FM device will make her job easier. The child will hear her better, and will be less likely to develop his own methods of leading the class.

The teacher has to know you realize that there are twenty-three other smiling faces in that classroom, all of equal importance to their parents. After devoting five years of your life, night and day, summer and winter, to getting the child to a level where he can be mainstreamed, it is hard not to try and impress on the teacher your expectations that such high-level input be maintained. That is not mainstreaming. Face it. The teacher will now have your child physically for the best learning times in the day. Your job of honing language and listening skills will continue after school.

Interview With a Kindergarten Teacher Who Has a Hard-of-Hearing Child in Her Class for the First Time.

PAM: Did you do any special preparation for this child?
TEACHER: In November I was sent by my school board to a school for the deaf for a two day course. It was fabulous. We listened to environmental, classroom and speech sounds through a hearing aid that was set up with the type of loss each child had. We had to do a spelling test, which most of us failed because we could not hear the words. We had

an overview of the methods used to teach children with hearing impairments to read. We were taught to read an audiogram. We were shown different types of hearing aids, and learned to use FMs in class. We were taught never to talk to the child from across the room. We learned about behavior problems and lags in social development because of a lag in speech and language.

PAM: What is the hearing loss of the child in your class?
TEACHER: The child has a mild/moderate loss in both ears, with fluctuations to severe when his middle ears are clogged. He develops accumulations of wax and has ventilation tubes which are always falling out.

PAM: Does the child always wear his hearing aids to school?
TEACHER: No. He usually appears with one aid and decides which ear he is going to wear it in.

PAM: How does he put a custom earmold for one ear in the other?
TEACHER: I don't know. The mother is very laid back about the child's hearing loss.

PAM: How does the child manage to hear in class?
TEACHER: Frequently he doesn't. I can tell because he is self-absorbed and non-reactive. When all systems are working well, he just lights up and is a joy to teach.

Thank you, Miss Basinstoke.

Dr. Ling is quite adamant in *Foundations of Spoken Language* that **two ears means two earmolds and two hearing aids**. Earmolds are custom designed for each ear and should never be interchangeable.

Principals

After Reid's second Brain Stem Auditory Evoked Response test, the principal and I collided in the school hall. She asked how things had gone. I replied, "He's hard of hearing." She questioned, "Well, how impaired is he? Will hearing aids help him? Will he need a special school? What about an FM?" I answered that we only knew a little about his good ear, but that there was plenty of hearing we could work with. Then I commented that her questions were pretty intense and asked why. She replied, "Because this child is going to be in my school in a few years and I want to have all the services we can, ready for him, when he gets here." Believe me, this principal's attitude and enthusiasm is "one in a million."

There was already one child with hearing aids in her school. The child was coping academically, but was treated badly in the school yard and his neighborhood. He had the additional disadvantage of being poor in a middle class venue, and had a terrible self image. We found out how bad the school yard was when William, then in kindergarten, came home with a black eye. "How did that happen?" his Dad asked. "Some kids were teasing Jeremy about his hearing aids and I said they should not do that. Daddy, will I have to get in fights when Reid goes to school?" Ross told him, "You must do what you think is right even if you get into trouble." I phoned the principal and related what William had said. The school learned a little about hearing problems and a lot about being nice. It is terribly hard to be the only child wearing hearing aids mainstreamed with regular children. Jeremy's life became much easier when another hard-of-hearing child moved into the school.

It is the principal's job to apply the directives and to administer the particular school system's policies. The principal is caught between the desires of the parents to maximize their child's potential through the public education system and the school system's desire to keep costs down. If the principal is primarily an educator, she may be more on the child's side. If she is an administrator, she may be more on the system's side.

Mainstreaming

"Mainstreaming" is an educational term used to describe putting a child with special needs in a regular classroom. It provides the child with a peer group of mostly ordinary children to play with and learn from, rather than a homologous peer group, say of children with hearing problems in a special school for those children. Mainstreaming, which all of us would like from an emotional point of view, makes good economic sense. If mainstreaming is interpreted only as putting the child in a class, maybe with an FM and relying on traditional progress reports to tell us when the child has failed, then mainstreaming has not helped the child.

If the principal and teachers view mainstreaming as an opportunity to recognize individual differences and can provide for them, the child's experiences will benefit him for the rest of his life.

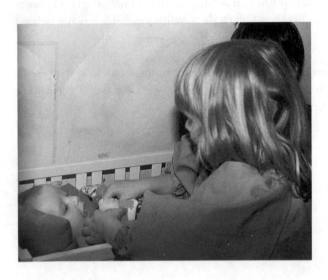

Chapter 6
A Parents' Eye View of
Hearing Tests

The Importance of Both Parents Attending Tests

Little in life is more important than the accurate early diagnosis of a
child's hearing problems. Both parents should be there. If the child ends
up without a hearing loss, you can celebrate together. If the test shows
the child is hard of hearing, you can hold onto each other, in what is
really a test of your marriage vows. Life has its good times and its bad
ones too. Having chosen each other for better, you need each other for
worse. If one spouse thinks the job is more important, think again. Next
year you might have a different job. You will still have the same child.

It is unfair to lay the burden of informing a spouse who cannot make
it to the test, on a parent who has just been plunged into grieving and
has had to make it home with the now hard-of-hearing child and instructions for getting hearing aids and earmolds. Being at the diagnostics makes the hearing problem very real to anyone concerned. Sitting

in the testing room while the child does not react to a sound is vivid proof of the loss. Not seeing the testing and being part of the process makes it easier to slip into denial and stay there for the rest of the child's life.

The audiologist should explain the test beforehand and the results afterwards. If it is possible, write down your concerns about the child's hearing. You will be asked to provide a medical history. If it is complicated, write all the pertinent details. The audiologist will talk to you about the child. The audiologist will often request your assistance in testing the child. Bring familiar "noise toys" such as a rattle, music box, tape recorded songs, or squeak toy to be used to elicit responses from your child. A parent's voice may also be used to see if the child will alert or attend to familiar phrases. The active participation of parents in the evaluation process is of great assistance to the professional and helps the parent to recognize, qualify, and finally acccept the child's hearing limitations. During this process, the audiologist will be explaining procedures and observations while the parent should feel free to ask questions. **That is the best advice. Ask questions.**

Assessing a Newborn Baby's Hearing

> The rest of your body slithered out in a rush
> You could move
> and cry
> You could open your eyes and see your mother
> and hear her voice . . .
> There were strange noises.
> But in the middle of all the other sounds
> was your mother's voice,
> one you already knew.
> **Sheila Kitzinger *Being Born*, (1986)**

In 1970, a joint committee of the American Speech-Language-Hearing Association,and the American Academy of Otolaryngology-Head and Neck Surgery and the American Academy of Pediatrics said that the costs and practical considerations involved did not warrant the routine use of neonatal testing (testing of newborn babies). A **High Risk Register** was developed to screen children at risk for hearing loss. A list of such risk factors follows:

1. Family history of hearing loss
2. Viral or other nonbacterial infections during pregnancy (e.g., rubella, cytomegalovirus, herpes, syphilis, toxoplasmosis)
3. Presence of head, facial, or external ear abnormalities
4. Low birth weight
5. High levels of bilirubin
6. Bacterial meningitis
7. Severe asphyxia, coma, seizures, or the need for continued ventilation

The American Speech-Language-Hearing Association (ASHA) suggested in 1988 that evaluation of these high-risk infants be carried out while still in the hospital, or in the first three months of life. (Martin, 1991)

In March of 1993, a Consensus Development Conference sponsored by the National Institute of Health further emphasized the importance of universal detection of hearing loss in infants and young children. The conference report underlined the importance of **early** detection because of the narrow window of opportunity to learn language (0–6 years), and the necessity of starting rehabilitation at the earliest possible moment. Free single copies of the complete NIH Consensus Statement on the Early Identification of Hearing Impairment in Infants and Young Children may be obtained from the Office of Medical Applications of Research, NIH, Federal Building Room 618, Bethesda, MD 20892

Indicators Associated with Sensorineural and/or Conductive Hearing Loss

A. For use with neonates (birth through age 28 days) when universal screening is not available.

1. Family history of hereditary childhood sensorineural hearing loss.
2. In utero infection, such as cytomegalovirus, rubella, syphilis, herpes, and toxoplasmosis.
3. Craniofacial anomalies, including those with morphological abnormalities of the pinna and ear canal.
4. Birth weight less than 1,500 grams (3.3 lbs).
5. Hyperbilirubinemia at a serum level requiring exchange transfusion.

6. Ototoxic medications, including but not limited to the aminoglycosides, used in multiple course or in combination with loop diuretics.
7. Bacterial meningitis.
8. Apgar scores of 0–4 at 1 minute or 0–6 at 5 minutes.
9. Mechanical ventilation lasting 5 days or longer.
10. Stigmata or other findings asssociated with a syndrome known to include a sensorineural and/or conductive hearing loss.

B. For use with infants (age 29 days through 2 years) when certain health conditions develop that require rescreening.

1. Parent/caregiver concern regarding hearing, speech, language and/or developmental delay.
2. Bacterial meningitis and other infections associated with sensorineural hearing loss.
3. Head trauma associated with loss of consciousness or skull fracture.
4. Stigmata or other findings associated with a syndrome known to include a sensorineural and/or conductive hearing loss.
5. Ototoxic medications, including but not limited to chemotherapeutic agents or aminoglycosides, used in multiple courses or in combination with loop diuretics.
6. Recurrent or persistent otitis media with effusion for at least 3 months.

C. For use with infants (age 29 days through 3 years) who require periodic monitoring of hearing.

Some newborns and infants may pass initial hearing screening but require periodic monitoring of hearing to detect delayed-onset sensorineural and/or conductive hearing loss. Infants with these indicators require hearing evaluation at least every 6 months until age 3 years, and at appropriate intervals thereafter.

Indicators associated with delayed-onset sensorineural hearing loss include:

1. Family history of hereditary childhood hearing loss.
2. In utero infection, such as cytomegalovirus, rubella, syphilis, herpes, or toxoplasmosis.
3. Neurofibromatosis Type II and neurodegenerative disorders.

Indicators associated with conductive hearing loss include:

1. Recurrent or persistant otitis media with effusion.
2. Anatomic deformities and other disorders that affect eustachian tube function.
3. Neurodegenerative disorders.

The above section on indicators is an excerpt cited from **The Joint Committee on Infant Hearing** *1994 Position Statement.*

> If you happen to be born in a certain state or in a large metropolitan hospital, or happen to be a graduate of an NICU (Neonatal Intensive Care Unit) you might have your hearing screened before six months of age. Even then, the probability that your hearing actually be screened depends on other extenuating factors such as: (1) Your parents' willingness and ability to bring you in for follow-up services; (2) If you have a primary care provider who is sensitive to the importance of early identification; (3) If the NICU you graduated from has standing hearing-screening orders; (4) If you have been identified as being at-risk for hearing loss; and (5) If your health insurance, your parents, or a public or private agency is willing to pay for the screening services.
> **Thomas B Mahoney** *Conference Papers of U.S. Office of Medical Applications of Research*, **(March, 1993).**

Researchers are focusing on cost, and the efficiency of methods available to test newborn hearing. As a parent I would like to say that the costs of newborn testing can never equal the costs of having a child with undiagnosed problems. So if you are the parents of a young baby who might have a hearing problem, see an audiologist as soon as possible. If you think your baby has a problem, and your professional does not agree, find another professional.

Brain Stem Auditory Evoked Response (BAER) Testing[1]

High-risk babies and babies who fail to respond to sound, from birth onwards, should be sent to the audiologist for BAER testing. Brain stem audiometry is possible at any age. Brain stem audiometry is a test of

---

[1]Professionals use multiple terms interchangeably for Brain Stem Auditory-Evoked Testing (BAER). These terms are: Brain Stem Response Testing(BSR); Auditory Brainstem Response(ABR); Brain Stem Evoked Response (BSER); and Evoked Response Audiometry (ERA).

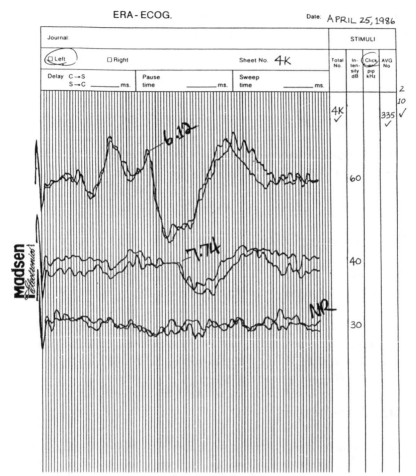

ERA - ECOG.

Date: APRIL 25, 1986

Figure 6.1 Printout of Auditory Evoked Brain Stem Response.
Decibels are listed at the right. Times marked are latency measures in
milliseconds. This is Reid's BAER for his ear with a mild loss.
Provided by Carol Pavey.

synchronous neural firings in response to sound. (Martin, 1991) For
brain stem audiometry, the child must be asleep.

The audiologist will put electrodes on the sleeping child to pick up the
brain's activity in response to thousands of clicks or tone pips. Extraneous responses are screened out by computer programs and repeata-
ble responses are averaged and presented in graph form. A tracing is
made on paper of the activity of the auditory center of the brain. The
fluctuation of certain waves are indicators of hearing ability. The au-

diologist will increase the volume until the child hears, or the machine reaches its limits, usually about 90 dB.

A BAER printout will look like this but much bigger. This is Reid's BAER for his "good"ear.

BAER testing is not usually used beyond the initial diagnosis of hearing loss in an individual who cannot give the responses required in other types of testing. Further testing, particularly at lower frequencies, must occur to corroborate the results and provide a basis for the selection of earmolds and hearing aids and audiological counseling.

Other Hearing Tests

Testing developed by audiologists can be logically divided into several groups: measurements of eardrum function; measurements of response to sounds; tests of speech. The audiologist can determine the type of hearing loss by interpretation of various tests. With a young child, testing is done frequently in the first few years. Once a child is old enough to say, "I hear that" the hearing testing becomes much easier.

Pure-Tone Testing

The audiometer is an electronic machine which produces different tones at variable degrees of loudness, controlled by the audiologist. A pure tone is a tone of only one frequency. The purpose of pure-tone testing is to find out how loud each tone has to be for the child to be able to hear it, or what is the quietest tone the child can hear. Pure-tone testing is done both by air and bone conduction to assess middle and inner ear function.

Air-Conduction Testing

Hearing tests which use sound travelling through the air into the ear canal, usually from headphones, are air-conduction tests. This is the most common kind of testing which measures deviation from the "norm."

Bone-Conduction Testing

Sound can be presented to the ear through a vibrator placed on the mastoid bone behind the ear. This is called bone-conduction testing and is done to determine if the hearing problem is in the outer or middle ear, rather than the inner ear. Sound transmitted through the mastoid bone is heard clearly by the cochlea, (inner ear). An "air-bone gap" or a difference between air-conduction testing and bone-conduction testing can indicate a defective outer or middle ear. This type of loss is referred to as a **conductive** hearing loss.

Threshold

The audiology department is quiet and the "cave" or echo-less, sound-proof chamber in which testing is carried out is very quiet, because the normal sounds of living are all muffled by sound barriers. This almost soundless environment is created in order to get an accurate assessment of the quietest sound a person can hear. This is called the hearing threshold.

Sound-Field Hearing Tests

It is likely that your child will have a traditional sound-field test, which consists of sound presented to the child through loud speakers in the testing room. This testing is done either after the BAER test to confirm results and expand information about other frequencies, or without BAER to begin with. Most children enjoy this. If your child is a baby, make sure he is well-fed and dry to minimize distractions.

At about four to six months of age, audiologists may try to interpret a baby's eye movements as responsive to sound. Meanwhile, the baby may be getting hungry, wet and bored. This is a very subjective area.

Head Phones

When the baby's head gets big enough, hearing tests will be done with headphones instead of loudspeakers. If the child is wearing headphones, the audiologist may give you an ear piece to listen to her instructions with, or your own pair of headphones. You may or may not hear the testing tones, or you may only hear them at one frequency and intensity.

Stimulus-Response Testing

Once a baby is aware enough to be alert to sound, around four months of age, a stimulus-response test using some form of reward for listening and looking is used: for example, a teddy bear which lights up. First the child is trained, with a sound that he can hear. At the sound of the tone, the teddy bear will be visible in the direction from which the sound came. The child learns he can see the bear light up when he hears the tone. So he hears the tone and looks for the bear. The audiologist can then use quieter and quieter sounds, at which the baby will continue to look for the bear, as long as he can hear. When he stops looking, either he cannot hear, or he is bored. There are other variations of S/R testing including food treats as a reward for hearing a tone, for older or diffi-cult-to-test children.

Speech Audiometry

Speech audiometry is the measurement of an individual's thresholds for speech. Testing materials for speech audiometry may include connected speech, two-syllable words, short words or sentences. Test results help to determine the extent of a hearing problem, tolerance and discrimi-nation for speech. Because young children are just learning to talk, special methods have been developed to test their speech. Speech-rec-ognition-threshold testing establishes the threshold of loudness at which spondees (two syllable words with equal emphasis on both syllables) are understood. Speech-detection-threshold testing establishes the lowest level at which selected words can be detected and identified as speech.

In 1970 Ross and Lerman developed the **Word Intelligibility by Pic-ture Identification (WIPI)** test for use with young children whose speech discrimination abilities cannot otherwise be tested. **WIPI** is done at louder-than-threshold levels. The audiologist has a book of pictures of things easily recognizable by the child, which can be easily confused by the child listening to the names. eg. **eye, pie, fly, tie**. The audiologist will say a word. The child must listen and point to the object. When the child's speech is further along, the audiologist will ask the child to repeat what she has said. The **Northwestern University Children's Perception of Speech (NU-CHIPS)** developed in 1980 by Elliot and Katz is similar to the **WIPI** and gaining in popularity according to Frederick Martin (1991).

Play Audiometry

Between babyhood and the time when a child can clap in response to a sound is a time when the audiologist must hone and fine tune the diagnostics with frequent retesting. The child becomes bored with S-R (Stimulus-Response) testing and simply refuses to listen. Early on, but not likely for the first round of diagnostics, you will be asked to train the child with play audiometry.

Play audiometry is doing a task in response to a sound. The audiologist usually has a collection of suitable toys such as pegboards, stacking rings, and shape sorters. The toy has to be complex enough to keep the child interested, but not so challenging that mastering the toy overides the task of listening for the sound, a delicate balance. If the audiologist is experienced with children, she will be able to find a game or toy which will keep the child interested. The parents and audiologist can discuss what is likely to work with the child on the day of testing. Reid once surprised me by sticking endless pegs into a peg board when he would never do that at home.

You teach play audiometry by holding a piece of the toy to your ear, making a noise within earshot, but out of visual range and saying, "I heard that. Did you hear that?" Then you put the ring on the stacker and pick up another piece which you give to the child. Show him to hold it near his ear, make the noise and wait for the child to show, "I heard that." Be sure that the noise you are making is audible to the child. If the child does not get the idea right away, keep on showing him and letting him have a turn until he gets the idea. If the child does not yet speak, he cannot say, "I hear that," but he should be capable of putting the ring on the stacker when he hears the sound. The whole family can get involved in learning to do something in response to the sound. Some children learn this in minutes and enjoy the game.

Reid liked doing play audiometry with his itinerant teacher. His playful attitude disappeared at the audiologist's office. Once we bought a shiny new red toy car and threatened to give it to the audiologist if he did not put the token in the box when he heard a sound. From age three to four years play audiometry was useful, but Reid was saying, "I hear that," consistently. After that his father took him to a hearing test and told him and the audiologist that Reid was to clap his hands or beep when he heard a sound, so the test would be finished sooner.

Tympanogram

The tympanum is the eardrum. A tympanogram tests the flexibility of the eardrum and the volume of the middle ear. The child sits still on a chair near the apparatus. The audiologist puts the correct size plug on the end of a wand and inserts it in the ear canal. Air-pressure levels in the ear canal are changed and the machine prints out the response of the eardrum. A tympanogram does not hurt, but might seem strange to the child. At a glance, the audiologist can tell how the eardrum is working and whether the child's middle ear is empty of fluid as it should be, or full of fluid.

If the child "fails" a tympanogram, you may go home with a referral to the ENT (ear, nose and throat doctor) to do something about the middle ear problems before proceeding with sensorineural testing. Another audiologist assured me that testing is done all the time with middle ear problems present, but my audiologist sent us home.

A child with a conductive loss or middle ear problems can be just as functionally hard of hearing as a child with a moderate sensorineural hearing loss. The difference is that with conductive loss, a cure is usually possible with drugs and/or surgery. Until the problem is cleared up and whenever it starts again, the child is hard of hearing. When the child's problems stem from the middle ear, the onus is on the parent to evaluate the child's hearing on a day-to-day basis. Stand ten feet away from the child and carry out the Ling Five-Sounds Test (See Chapter 7) while the child claps in response or repeats what he has heard. If the child is missing any sounds, take him to the doctor that day. Every day that the child does not hear well because of middle ear problems, is a day lost in his foundation of language—the minimal auditory deficiency syndrome. (Martin, 1991) It is well known that hard-of-hearing and deaf children have a much higher incidence of middle ear problems than the normally-hearing population, and these often go unnoticed.

In-the-Ear Probe-Microphone Testing

A hearing aid sitting in a human ear behaves differently than a hearing aid sitting in a electroacoustic test box. For this reason tiny probe microphones have been developed to test the function of the hearing aid while it is in the ear.

The child's personality as well as the resources of the institution testing the child will determine whether a child has his hearing aids evaluated with the help of an in-the-ear probe-microphone. Reid's last audiologist would not consider probe-microphone testing for him because he was difficult. So we went elsewhere because I had seen it used during a seminar presented by Dan Ling. Despite Reid's abilities to be a true stinker at the audiologist, he was not the least concerned about having the probe microphone inserted. In fact, he said it tickled.

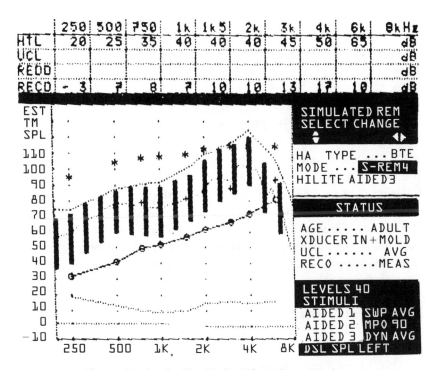

Figure 6.2 In-the-Ear Probe-Microphone Testing.
Shows the function of the hearing aid as it is used in the ear,
rather than an acoustic box.
Provided by S. Moodie

The child sits on a chair. He must sit still while the audiologist inserts a thin tube into the ear canal almost up to the eardrum. The earmolds are inserted. A few buttons are pushed, the machine presents a full sound run, like a delicate slide whistle with stops. The computer prints out the hearing aid's performance through all the sounds just presented, plus the resonance of the ear and the interactions of these effects. The audiologist has a baseline threshold to which is added the desired gain in volume to reach the CLEAR (Conversational Level Elements in the Acoustic Range, See Chapter 7, CLEAR and the "Speech Banana") zone plus the ear's use of the outer ear, (which is lost by the plug of the earmold and so must be included in the calculation). The audiologist then adjusts the small screws inside the hearing aid, (which you, as parents, should not touch) and can change the output of the aid. It's neat to see the child hooked up to this machine, complete with sound effects, then watch the audiologist get out his screw driver and adjust the aids while they are sitting on the child's head and have instant feedback as to what each little turn of the screw is doing. The best quality of amplification is what the professionals are seeking. For speech within earshot, in-the-ear probe-microphone tuning gives us that quality.

The Parent's Role in Testing

A hearing test is one time when you must let the little bird fly alone. You are trying to find out how well the child hears. It is not a Pass/Fail situation or any reflection on the child if he does not do well. If you tell the child the answer, the audiologist cannot assess the child's hearing. Once in a while you will anyway because parents are like that, but try hard not to cue the child. Audiologists are pretty sharp and will usually catch you and invalidate that part of the test.

Behavioral Considerations

Probably, many children enjoy hearing tests. Whether it is the "Sit here! Do this! Listen!" or because we are testing a part of him that does not work well, Reid hates hearing tests. In every other situation in life he has vision, context, speechreading, and situational clues. He is master of them all. In the testing room he is only using one sense which is hard for him. We must test his hearing and cannot allow his compensating

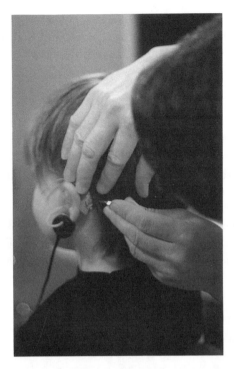

Figure 6.3 In-the-Ear Probe-Microphone Testing.
It is fascinating to see the audiologist use his tiny screwdriver to adjust the
hearing aids right on the child's head.
Photo by PAM Candlish

tactics. No matter how nice, or demanding, or bribing, or punitive we
are, he will not cooperate. I feel failure as a good parent when the child
is rude to a perfectly nice person who wants to help. This builds with
each appointment, especially if the appointment is a make-up session
for an incomplete hearing test because of behavior a month before.

At the urban general hospital where our audiology was done for some
time, there was a waiting room with a snack bar. We never had to wait
for long, Reid has a reputation. Reid would see the snack bar and ask
for a soft drink. A soft drink is not the best thing to have before a
hearing test, because the child might have to use the bathroom in the
middle of the test which breaks up or ends the session. So I say, "no soft
drink" and Reid gets mad at me. Then the audiologist comes and gets
us. Reid is coy, rude, distrustful and uncooperative.

If your child is good at the audiologist's, count your blessings. If he is badly behaved, have a hearing test yourself and find out how hard he has to work, even though he is just a little kid who should be in the park.

There has been a great deal of research and thought into the special needs of children. Just about all of the audiologists I have worked with have a member of their family with hearing problems. They have a great sense of compassion and empathy for a hard-of-hearing child. Our former audiologist always finished up a test with the music from **Sesame Street,** as a reward for listening well.

I have relied heavily on Martin's text *Introduction to Audiology*, 4th Ed, (1991) for the information in this chapter. I am also grateful to Shane Moodie, our audiologist at the University of Western Ontario for his explanations and help.

Chapter 7
The Audiogram: A Scientific
Picture of the Child's Hearing
The Ling Five-Sounds Test

Until the early part of this century, "deaf" described people who did not hear. There were people who tried to find ways to teach deaf people to communicate. Sign languages were developed to replace the spoken word. This was promoted by Gallaudet. Also, there was the oral approach using speech sounds. This was the method advanced by Alexander Graham Bell. Most of what we do today is based on one of these methods, but we have advanced at a phenomenal rate in the past forty years.

A diagnosis of significant hearing loss in the 1950's was a description of the percentages of hearing lost or available. The audiologist's bells and whistles were crude, as were hearing aids. Powerful hearing aids were enormous, because of the electronics and the batteries. Small hearing aids were practically useless.

My grandfather, Dr. E.M. Morgan, one of the early roentgenologists, was deaf and blind at least partly from radiation from X-ray equipment. My father insisted my grandfather always have the latest development in electronic hearing aids. Earmolds were standardized, the hearing aid a small box to fit in a shirt pocket. Whenever Dad visited his father, he would insist that the hearing aid be used, but my grandfather preferred his ear trumpet, except to listen to the six o'clock news. I can remember battles between father and son. "Why won't you use the hearing aids I buy for you?" "Because they don't work very well!" The hearing aids of the 1950's and 1960's did not work well enough to inspire an intelligent, educated man to use them. Speech for a prelingually hard-of-hearing child seemed an impossibility.

There were some specialists like Doreen Pollack, Helen Beebe, Daniel Ling, and others who believed it possible to get sounds loud enough for the deaf child to hear them. Audiologists needed to know exactly what the child could hear. Hearing tests became more accurate and related to the sounds of speech rather than gross sounds like bells and whistles. Scientists measured the sounds of speech and plotted them on a chart called an audiogram. An individual's hearing ability could be charted in relationship to these important speech sounds and could be estimated with considerable confidence.

Think about all the sounds in your life. An audiogram is a graphic representation of pure-frequency sounds: high or low, loud or soft.

Sound is a physical event consisting of frequency, intensity and duration. Frequency is measured in cycles per second or Hertz (Hz). One Hz equals one cycle per second. It measures the number of times a sound wave, (source) vibrates in one second. If you stretch an elastic tightly and pluck it, in a way, you can see the frequency of the sound it makes. You cannot see the actual number of vibrations because your eye is not fast enough. You will see a blurred outline of the shape of the sound wave. Very low sounds have low Hz. The low sound at the beginning of Richard Strauss' *"Also Sprach Zarathustra"* is about 25 Hz, middle C on a piano is 261.62 Hz.

Intensity is how loud the sound is, usually measured in decibels (dB). Decibels were the concept of Alexander Graham Bell. Turning up a radio increases the intensity of the sound, or the number of decibels you are listening to. Most of us think of sound as loud or soft, loud or

Ear trumpets from the library of the Alexander Graham Bell
Association for the Deaf.

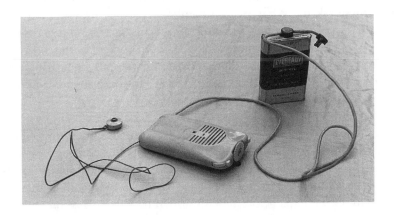

Electronic Hearing Aid 1950's.

**Figure 7.1 Ear Trumpets and Electronic Hearing Aid:
Ancient and Recent History.**
Photos by PAM Candlish

quiet. The higher the number of decibels, the louder the sound. One decibel is just audible, the faintest sound a good human ear can hear, and no decibels is silence.

Measures of frequency and intensity are plotted on an audiogram. Duration, which is how long the sound continues, is not shown. In sound-field testing the tones can be long or short, partly dependent on the age of the child and partly on the degree of difficulty anticipated in hearing the sound.

Nearly all of the speech sounds of English are represented on an audiogram in an area called the "speech banana." If you squint at a graph of little marks designating sounds of speech, plotted according to their frequency and intensity, the little marks will blur together into an area that looks like a banana. The "speech banana" is also called the Conversational Level Elements in the Acoustic Range of speech zone or the CLEAR zone.

Ling Five Sounds and the Ling Five-Sounds Test

Reid had wax in one ear which necessitated a trip to a new ear/nose and throat doctor. After I installed the aid in the unblocked ear I said **"ah ee ou sh ss."** Reid clapped after each sound to show he had heard. The nurse asked, "What are you doing?" I answered, "The Ling Five-Sounds test to determine the function of the hearing aid across the speech spectrum." She commented, "I have worked in this office for twenty years. I have seen thousands of people put in hearing aids. I have never seen anyone do that. What were those sounds again?" I wrote **"ah ee ou sh ss"** down on a card.

Our other children equate **ah ee ou sh ss**, with "Bippity Boppity Boo," and will incant the oath to do their bit for better hearing. We have learned that better hearing for Reid ensures a nicer next day for us all. I wonder if Ling realizes that there are parents chanting **ah ee ou sh ss** every night. Perhaps before he falls alseep he says a **ah ee ou sh ss** for all the hard-of-hearing children in the world.

So what is this ritual? I think of it as the astronomy of speech. William can look at the sky, find the North Star and a number of constellations, because he has learned to recognize certain patterns of stars and

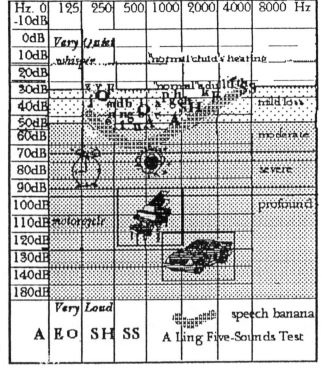

Hertz indicates how low or high the sound is.

Decibels measure how loud or quiet a sound is.

Most of the speech sounds are clustered in an area called the speech banana or CLEAR zone, although some of the higher frequency sounds like f, th, ss run off the chart.

The sounds of things are graphed for intensity only.
Speech sounds graphed for intensity and frequency in one format.

Ling Five Sounds graphed for first and second format.
from **Hearing in Children**. Northern & Downs. 1978.
Ling: lectures and books.

Figure 7.2 Audiogram Showing Some Environmental and Speech Sounds (in One Diagram); Ling Five-Sounds Test.
Unitron pamphlet, PAM and Les Candlish Graphics

planets. He tells me they are always in the same place at the same time of year. I look at the sky and see stars. The pattern of a constellation enables him to recognize it from the other stars in the sky. Ling's Five Sounds are like the stars in a constellation. They are always in the same place, holding to the pattern of the "speech banana" from the low sounds **oo** and **ee** to the highest sounds of **sh** and **ss**. So by having the child respond to or repeat these sounds, you are sampling how the hearing aid transmits across the entire CLEAR zone.

At age five Reid often will not clap for me at home. He usually repeats what he has heard. Sometimes he twiddles his baby toe or raises an eyebrow. One day I forgot his hearing aids and had to take them in to school. I said "**ah, ee oo sh ss**," and he clapped for each sound. Reid's teacher uses the Five-Sounds Test each morning when the FM is hooked up. When the microphone is moved from teacher to teacher, it is retested each time it is reconnected. If the child is accurate, which is built up with continuous practice, then the technology used in class is kept in prime condition.

At age six, Reid repeats each of the Five Sounds as he hears them. We also use a "pass-word" which varies from day to day, but contains many of the high frequency sounds he can have trouble hearing such as "cats spit." When he has a cold, the additional complication of conductive loss removes his **ss** and **sh**. "Ghostbusters" becomes "Gobuer."

I have suggested to the large number of my friends who have children with fluctuating hearing due to otitis media, that if they do the Ling Five-Sounds Test in a normal voice at twenty feet, every morning, they have an instant assessment of how well the child's ears are going to work today. Having a child who uses hearing aids lends me a little credibility so some were willing to try. To their amazement, when the child's ears were filling up, the child stopped clapping to **sh** and **ss**. How much information gets obliterated in the classroom for these children?

A child who cannot hear a **ss** or **sh** at twenty feet may need to have an FM unit in class, or be moved to a desk nearest to the teacher, providing the child can hear at ten feet. A child who cannot hear an **ee** or **ah** at twenty feet should go to the doctor instead of going to school. When these children get diagnosed as having a fluctuating loss, usually nothing is done beyond preferential seating, unless the child becomes a monster in class. Then the proposed methods are behavior-oriented, which are inappropriate because the problem is that the child cannot hear. "**Ah ee oo sh ss**" takes ten seconds, costs nothing and ensures that the occasionally hard-of-hearing child will be able to hear his world today.

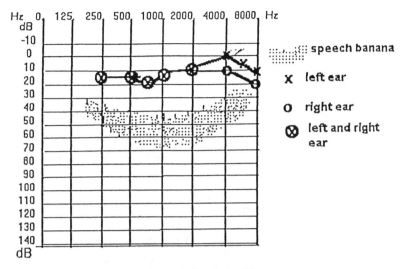

Figure 7.3 William's Audiogram.

This is Reid's older brother, William's, audiogram. As you can see he has pretty good hearing. He hears very high, quiet sounds better in his left ear, and his threshold is the same for both ears for sounds below 2000 Hz.

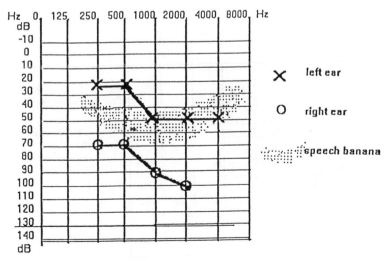

Figure 7.4 Reid's Unaided Audiogram.

This is one of Reid's audiograms on page 63. It has always annoyed me that I have never seen one like it in a book, so for all parents with a child with an unequal loss, here is an example of that kind of audiogram.

On most audiograms, **X** is used to mark the findings for the left ear and **O** is used for the right ear. Some audiologists use red and blue pens but the differences in ink color do not show up on a photocopy, so it has become customary to use **X** and **O** to indicate the unaided threshold for each ear.

The unaided threshold is a picture of the absolutely quietest sound a person can hear, in a perfect acoustic environment. Add about 30 dB to this line to get a ball park figure of roughly what the child can hear without hearing aids in the real world. Lots of parents never get beyond looking at the child's unaided threshold, but this is really a concern for the audiologist.

The lines which are important for you to remember and understand, are the aided thresholds, which show what the child can hear when

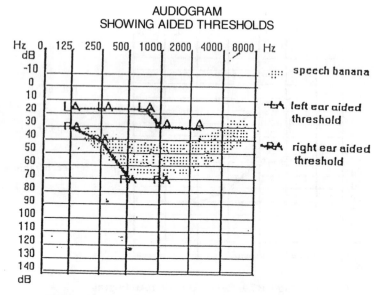

AUDIOGRAM
SHOWING AIDED THRESHOLDS

Figure 7.5 Audiogram Showing Aided Thresholds.

wearing hearing aids, in an acoustically perfect environment. Find your child's aided thresholds relative to each speech sound. The aided thresholds should be the lines closest to 0 dB and 125 hz. Remember! What the child can or cannot hear is not as black and white as the lines on an audiogram. Perfect acoustic backgrounds exist only in audiologists' testing rooms. In the real world, sounds will be harder to hear than the audiogram would make you think.

Look at the aided thresholds while remembering where the "speech banana" or CLEAR zone is. In the above aided audiogram, the child would be able to hear everything but **ss** and **sh** with his left ear. With his right ear, he would only hear the low sounds of the first formant of **oo** and **ee.**

Of course he has a "good" ear and would rely on it for the development of language. This is called "better ear." Audiologists prescribing hearing aids for children with markedly different hearing in each ear, usually put an aid on each ear, according to the ear's requirements. Other professionals like the educational group, tend to look at the "better ear's" ability.

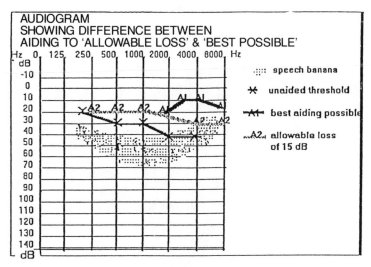

Figure 7.6 Audiogram Showing Difference Between Allowable Loss and Best Aiding Possible.

I assumed Reid's good ear would automatically get good amplification. I was surprised when the new audiologist expressed interest in his good ear. Look at the difference between aiding to an allowable loss of 15 dB which was standard practice in Canada, and aiding for best hearing possible. We also put a new earmold on this ear, even though the old one was not yet outgrown and a Libby horn (a specialized part of the earmold) to increase the high-frequency sounds even more. With in-the-ear-probe-microphone tuning, a new earmold, and a different protocol, Reid's new hearing aid is ready for the race track of life, with almost a full spectrum of sound available to him, within earshot.

When we first started out, I did not understand what all the lines meant on an audiogram. Another human being is putting on paper, what happens to sound in your child's world. Understanding the aided audiogram is your first step in coping with the inner world of a hard-of-hearing child.

Chapter 8
The Ear, Ear Canal, Eardrum, Middle Ear and Inner Ear. Didn't I Learn This in Grade Six, "Health?"

The Outer Ear

The outer ear is important because it is where you plug in the earmold and hang the hearing aid. A child wearing hearing aids does not walk into doors and other obstacles more than other children, but it seems so. The hearing aid is hard and the ear soft. The hearing aid wins, the ear gets hurt. Before earmolds were made of soft silicone, blood could be shed in any encounter from the inside of the outer ear. The hearing aid could not be used until the ear healed.

When the outer ear gets hurt by the hearing aid, put a corn plaster on the plastic casing of the aid to keep it off the skin of the outer ear until the sore spot has healed.

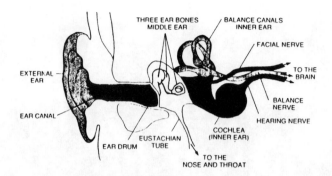

THREE EAR BONES
MIDDLE EAR

BALANCE CANALS
INNER EAR

FACIAL NERVE

EXTERNAL
EAR

TO THE
BRAIN

EAR CANAL

BALANCE
NERVE

HEARING NERVE

EUSTACHIAN
TUBE

COCHLEA
(INNER EAR)

EAR DRUM

TO THE
NOSE AND THROAT

Figure 8.1 Diagram of the Ear.
Graphics courtesy of Unitron

The audiologist said she had never seen anything like it, when I showed her a deep abrasion (almost a hole) in Reid's ear caused by the hearing aid's constant rubbing. If the hearing aid rubs on the ear and irritates it, get some super moleskin, made by **Dr. Scholl**. The backing is adhesive and it is easy to cut a piece to exactly fit the back of the aid, with just a bit around the sides. We put corn plasters under the moleskin to change the shape of the aid too. This made his hearing aids look hokey, but stopped the irritation.

Keep an eye out for slight pinkening of the skin, or a collection of bumps. There is a slight possibility that the child may be allergic to the materials used for earmolds, hooks, tubing, and casing for the hearing aid. The materials are tested for hypoallergenic properties. The child might be allergic to adhesives used to keep moleskins on or to hold the hearing aids close to the scalp. I used little rolls of adhesive tape between Reid's hearing aid and his scalp when he was a baby. He was allergic to several brands of adhesive tape. The better the tape held the hearing aids on his head, the faster he developed a reaction. He never developed an allergy to the hypoallergenic tapes, but they never kept the aids in place. Double-sided surgical adhesive tape is non-irritating and strong.

As the child grows, the hearing aids will stay on his head better. You can get special hooks which will keep the hearing aids in place through a football game. We take the hearing aids out in active situations like skating, skiing, and bicycling.

The boots (connectors) to the FM extend the bottom of the hearing aid by one-half-inch and provide a new area to be checked for irritation. You may need to apply moleskin to the part of the boot near the ear, even if the hearing aids are not causing any problems. If the child wears an FM at school, keep an eye on the part of the ear below the hearing aid, where the boots fit in place.

Ear Wax

Hearing aid earmolds are foreign bodies lodged in the child's ear canals. The ear canal tries to get rid of the earmold by producing ear wax. An unaided ear sheds ear wax because it does not have a plug in it. Human ear wax comes in a variety of colors, depending on the chemistry of the body producing it: dark orange, gold, yellow or green. The pretty new earmolds will take on the color of the child's ear wax because the earmold is in contact with ear wax all the time. I hate it when Reid's earmolds yellow because they never look clean. Often when the earmolds are removed from the child's ears, pieces of ear wax will adhere at the end of the earmold or in the hole. Mild soap and water will clean the earmolds.

Wax in the ear canal can build up and harden, blocking sound from the hearing aid. If the aids start feeding back,(making a squealing sound) ear wax buildup might be the cause. How can you look into the ear canals to check for wax buildup? Due to a black spot in the middle of the beam, the average flashlight provides lots of light on the outer ear and little light down the child's ear canal. As soon as you pull on the child's outer ear to straighten the ear canal and get the light aimed down the ear canal so you can see, the child will move. And what are you looking at anyway?

Get a flashlight which does not have a black circle in the middle of the beam. Doctors have a flashlight called an otoscope with a cone to put into the ear canal and special optics for bright light. Make an appointment with your doctor and take your flashlight and child with you. Get the doctor to show you what nice, clean healthy ear canals look like through the otoscope. Compare what you are seeing with what you can see with your flashlight. Then look at the ear canals on a regular basis. If anything looks different, take the child to the doctor.

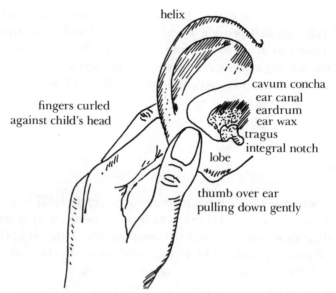

Figure 8.2 What You Can See With a Good Flashlight.
Drawing by PAM Candlish

Our family doctor has written a prescription for an otoscope for me, (We had to pay for it ourselves.) and gave me a good lesson in the use of an otoscope. Your hand which is holding the ear to straighten the ear canal should have the rest of your fingers curled against the child's head to prevent sudden movement. If you are going to use an otoscope, it is important to learn from an expert. Dr. David Marty gives a good lesson in *The Ear Book* (1987).

A plug of wax can be pushed down the ear canal until it reaches the eardrum. The child might take the earmolds out repeatedly or scream in pain. The child might not do anything, a problem because the potential for damage to the eardrum is high. About once a week check on ear wax build up with your flashlight.

There does not seem to be a treatment of choice for getting rid of ear wax. One doctor suggests warm water and peroxide, a second expresses horror at peroxide and suggests just warm water, a third prefers warm oil, while a fourth suggests a product to soften the ear wax called **Cerumwax** and syringing with water. It is my job to look at the child's ears and the doctor's job to clean them out. If your child has ventilation tubes through his eardrums, never attempt to deal with ear wax yourself.

One of our ear, nose, and throat doctors described the outer ear with a hearing aid in it as being like a greenhouse in which fungi were deliriously happy. Warm and damp is home sweet home to these organisms. Take the child to the doctor, and keep the ear canals drier. When the child takes his hearing aids out to sleep, his ears will have those hours to dry out. The doctor will prescribe ear drops as long as the child does not have ventilation tubes. Removing the aids and thorough washing and drying the earmolds and tubing several times throughout the day may help. Clean the earmolds carefully as reinfection can come from fungi which hide in all the nooks and crannies.

The last thing you can see with your flashlight is the eardrum at the back of the ear canal. It looks grayish white except when the child is crying or has an ear infection. Then it becomes bright red. If the child has ventilation tubes, you can see them.

Ventilation Tubes

In the case of persistent middle ear infection the doctor may install ventilation tubes through the eardrum to reduce the severity of otitis media or chronic middle ear infections. Otitis media is very common, especially in children under the age of three, because their eustachian tubes do not drain downwards, just across. If you put a straw into a glass of water and seal the end with your finger, you can lift a whole straw full of water out of the glass without spilling a drop. When you take your finger off the end of the straw, all the water will fall out. This is the theory behind ventilation tubes through the eardrum. By allowing a little air into the middle ear there is no longer a vacuum holding the eustachian tubes full of mucous. The fluids should drain out of the middle ear.

Children are typically treated for recurrent otitis media with a three-month course of two different antibiotics and decongestants throughout, before resorting to surgery. I found that ten days of antibiotics will not do it for Reid. The child is back at the doctor's with another ear infection on the twelfth day. It is not another ear infection, it is the same infection, sometimes doubled in ferocity by ineffective antibiotic treatment.

I do not believe the human ear has changed so drastically that we must surgically insert tubes through the ear drum, making a hole where there is not supposed to be one. However, we are assaulted by air pollution every time we breathe, coming from cars and factories. It is very possible that we have a generation of little children's noses trying to deal with poisoned air, and constantly dripping noses lead to blocked eustachian tubes and otitis media.

A child with recurrent middle-ear infections should see a doctor who specializes in allergies. Cow's milk is often found to be a factor, especially when the child is little and gets so much nutrition from our friend, the cow.

I found having a child with ventilation tubes was disrupting. The child must not get his ears wet. Water that gets into the ear canals goes through the eardrums via the tubes and causes a new infection. You can get plugs made at the hearing aid dealer which are the same as earmolds and cost about the same. As long as they fit perfectly and the child does not submerge, the ears will stay dry. They will fit perfectly just as long as the child's earmolds do. You can also get wax plugs which shape to the child's ear, at any drug store, which will keep water out as long as the plug stays in. The child hears less with plugs in his ears. The child has to wear plugs for swimming, bathing, showering, shampooing, playing in the wading pool, and any other time he might get wet. Even getting caught in a rainstorm is fraught with stress in case a raindrop gets in.

We found the threat of water started to control what we did. Reid's hair hardly was washed, we stopped swimming as a family. When the last tube fell out, we had a hydrophobic child who would not get wet, even in the bathtub. He could not learn to swim because he spent so long holding his head out of water that he could not relax and float. Reid has scarring on both his eardrums from the surgery, which is significant on his good ear. (I would like to know how great the drop in efficiency of his eardrum is, as a result of surgery.)

Reid's tympanograms were the basis of the recommendation for ventilation tubes. He never showed distress, no piercing screaming, no rubbing or pulling on his ear, no fever, no red spots until the tubes were in place. After the tubes fell out for the last time he never had another middle ear infection. The whole family went to the audiologist's and had slightly negative tympanograms. If it had just been Reid, he would have gone home to decongestants, but it was the rest of the gang. The audiologist said it must be the machine. I revealed to her that we had driven down hill to her office, a drop of some twelve hundred feet.

Some children do so much better with ventilation tubes. The doctors are not always overenthusiastic about putting them in. I know one child quite well who fails in school the years he does not have tubes in his ears. His mother is not at all inconvenienced by the same things which drove me up the wall. She thinks tubes are the cat's meow.

If your child has ventilation tubes and hearing aids in his ears, you must be scrupulous in your hygiene of the earmolds and ear canals. Some medicines used to cure fungal infections are ototoxic, meaning they can cause further deafness if used in ears with ventilation tubes. Before using anything for your child's ears, even a prescription, look up the drug in the *PDR (Physicians Desk Reference)* an official medical book describing drugs and medicines. Your pharmacist and your doctor should have the newest edition. Listed under each drug are side effects to that drug. There are also contra-indications listed, meaning conditions which prohibit the use of that particular drug. Check the side effects and the contra-indications looking for the words ototoxic, hearing loss, or ventilation tubes. Because this information is only available for prescription drugs, do not ever put anything into your child's ears which you cannot look up first, even if you can buy it "over the counter."

Blowing the nose, blocking off one nostril with a finger, while blowing hard, can lead to recurrent middle ear infections. The finger blocking the nostril is only preventing air from coming out the nose, while the back of the nose where the eustachian tubes drain into is quite open. So all that extra pressure is just as likely to send the mucous up the eustachian tubes, as out one nostril. Wipe the child's nose and tell him not to blow. You might have fewer middle ear infections.

Chapter 9
Hearing Aids
and Aids to Hearing

Behind-the-Ear Aid

The most commonly used hearing aid with children is the behind-the-ear (BTE) type which consists of a little colored plastic case with switches and a volume control, a battery case, microphone and speaker attached to a plastic hook which may have an acoustic filter, which attaches to a plastic tube which goes into a custom-made earmold, which fits into the child's ear. The little plastic casing hangs on the back of the ear, between the pinna (the cartilaginous projecting part of the external ear) and the scalp.

The casing can be matched to skin color, hair color, or be selected as the child's favorite color. Reid's current aid is transparent red. He likes the colorless transparent covers best, but we have difficulty getting them in Canada. The last casing replacement was at Christmas so he went with red. He also pointed out that his name means red, so he was pleased with his red aid. Reid is now eleven. Our friend Peter now has BTE

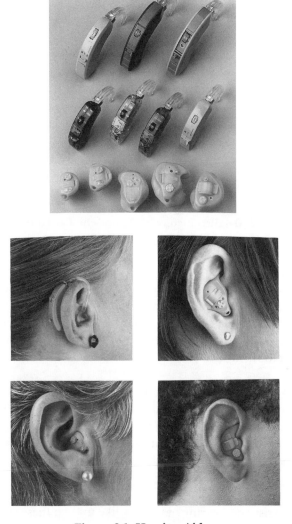

Figure 9.1 Hearing Aids.
Hearing aid styles include regular behind-the-ear, custom-in-the-ear-canal,
low profile, and mini behind-the-ear. The four little pictures show
how some aids look being used.
Photo courtesy of Unitron

aids. I showed him Reid's red aid. Peter looked at it with disgust and said, "It is supposed to match your skin or hair so it will not show as much." Reid is equally disgusted with beige plastic. Ask the child about casing colors if you can.

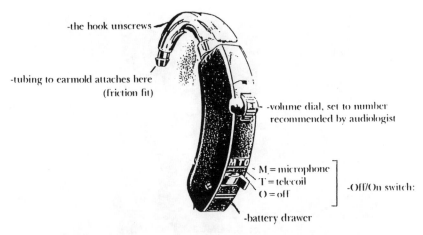

-the hook unscrews

-tubing to earmold attaches here
(friction fit)

-volume dial, set to number
recommended by audiologist

M = microphone
T = telecoil
O = off

-Off/On switch:

-battery drawer

Figure 9.2 Detailed Picture of Behind-the-Ear Hearing Aid.
Photo courtesy of Unitron

Only the audiologist or hearing aid dealer should remove the cover which protects the dials used to tune the aids. If the hearing aid is not working, which you determine by listening with a special stethoscope to the sound or lack of sound coming out of the speaker/receiver, take the hearing aid to the dealer.

You must know what the hearing aid can do. You will see the function of the hearing aid when it is analysed in a test box by the hearing aid dealer or the audiologist. The hearing aid is placed in the box and given a full run of sound at 60 dB through all the frequencies. A strip of paper comes out of the testing equipment which looks something like this.

The audiologist and hearing aid dealer like to keep these strips in their files. Convince the professional to let you have a strip for each hearing aid, when the hearing aids are new. Then you will have a baseline to compare with when the hearing aids get older. If you have a copy of these strips, you will have proof the hearing aid did not always output in this strange new manner it has developed. If the strips have always looked about the same and start to look different, it is easy to understand that the hearing aids are functioning differently. You do not need to understand all the quirks of the read-outs, a general understanding is enough. Decibels are printed up the side, and frequency along the bottom.

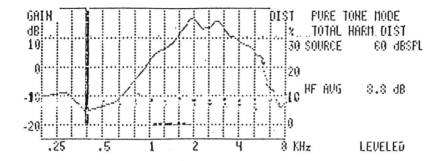

The hearing aid is tested in a "box" which shows how well the hearing aid is working. The acoustic gain of a hearing aid is the difference in dB between an input signal and an output signal. The volume of the hearing aid is set and a sound of 60 dB is given to the aid. Loudness or intensity is shown up the graph and pitch or frequency across the bottom. Frederick Martin, *Introduction to Audiology*, 1991.

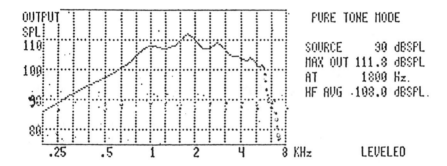

The SSPL or Saturation Sound-Pressure Level test measures the maximum sound produced by the hearing aid. Damage to the child's ear would result if this were not carefully set. The aid is turned to full volume and an input signal of 90 dB SPL is used. Frederick Martin, *Introduction to Audiology*, 1991.

Figure 9.3 Electro-Acoustic Testing of Hearing Aid.
Printouts provided by S. Moodie

BTE hearing aids have many advantages. The sound source is on the child's ear where the child would hear naturally and they are unobtrusive. BTE aids are delicate and do not like to be dropped or get wet. Cracks in the casing causes irregular or constant feedback. It is easy to break off the battery casing. Sometimes this requires a whole new casing for the aid and sometimes only a new battery drawer is needed.

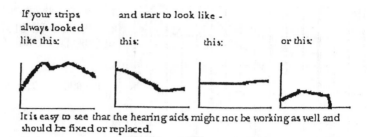

If your strips
always looked
like this: and start to look like -   this: this: or this:

It is easy to see that the hearing aids might not be working as well and should be fixed or replaced.

Figure 9.4 Electro-Acoustic Testing Showing Varied Output From One Hearing Aid.

Ask your dealer to get you the pamphlet which shows the products for children. If the company does not offer products for children, such as smaller hooks and plastic volume-control covers, ask the dealer to issue a complaint to the company.

Stethoscope

When you buy the aids, buy a stethoscope so you can listen to them. These come in two varieties. One looks just like the doctors' tool, with two plugs for your ears and a little bell plug at the end to place over the speaker or hook. The newer stethoscopes have only one plug for your ear. Mine has two earplugs, but just a long piece of plastic tubing. (Did you know that doctors determined how long the tubing was on a stethoscope was by how high a flea could jump?)

Figure 9.5 Kiddihooks.
Hearing aid retainer, a device to foil a youngster's attempts to remove the hearing aids.
Photo courtesy of Phonak

Figure 9.6 Stethoscope.
Many parents find this inexpensive "stethoscope" a convenient accessory for
daily listening checks. The listening tube with its one-size eartip
fits most adult ears.
Photo courtesy of Unitron

All kidding aside, the longer the tube, the greater the drop in decibels
put out by the hearing aid. So a parent with normal hearing and a child
with a powerful set of aids should have long tubes on the stethoscope
to protect the parents' hearing. Turn the hearing aid off while attaching
it to the tubing and turn the volume down. Once the tubing is attached
to the hearing aid, turn the hearing aid on and slowly turn up the
volume. There should be no hissing. Sounds should be clear. If you find
it unpleasant to listen to the hearing aid at the volume that the child
uses it, get longer tubing. I have the reverse problem with Reid's hearing
aid. His hearing loss and mine are becoming similar and I have trouble
telling whether the hearing aid is on. Obviously if my ears get worse,
someone with better ears will have to take over.

In-the-Ear and In-the-Canal Aids

Few children have in-the-ear hearing aids which go into the external ear canal. Children outgrow these hearing aids at the same speed that earmolds have to be replaced, but it is much more expensive to change to a slightly larger hearing aid, than to replace an earmold. The child would have to have be willing to sit still for lengthy periods. Hearing aid professionals are dead set against in-the-canal and in-the-ear hearing aids on most young children.

Cochlear Implants

Many of us have very little idea of what a cochlear implant is, but suspect it might be some kind of invisible hearing aid which works really well, compared to the BTE hearing aids. So far this is not true. A cochlear implant does not work better than a hearing aid, but it works as well as a hearing aid. A hearing aid takes sound and makes it louder. A cochlear implant takes sound and translates it into electrical pulses which are presented to the nerves in the cochlea. It is useful to people who get no improvement in hearing from regular hearing aids.

The first cochlear implant was a single channel device, developed by Dr. William House and his colleagues in Los Angeles. Current cochlear implants have multi-channels. The multi-channel implant provides much more information on the frequency components of speech. It is easier for the user to decode what he is listening to with more information coming through. Cochlear implants still need a lot of development, but there are numerous researchers in many countries working long and late to make them even better.

The cochlea is the part of the inner ear which looks like a snail shell. If you were to unroll the cochlea, you would find that it is quite long with little nerves strung on membranes throughout its length. The nerves at the beginning are longer than the nerves at the end. High-frequency sounds are picked up by the nerves near the outer end, mid-frequency sounds by the nerves in the middle and low-frequency sounds by the nerves at the inner end. Each frequency of sound has its own receptor nerves, unless the hearing has been damaged, in which case there will be gaps. The normal cochlea function is to convert sound vibrations received by the middle ear into nerve impulses that will travel along the auditory nerve to the auditory centers of the brain.

Part of the cochlear implant must be surgically placed in the cochlea. The implanted electrodes look like a fine wire with tiny scales on them. This is attached to an internal coil which is embedded in the bone of the skull just above the ear. An external coil attaches magnetically through the skin and is joined by a wire to the speech processor, the brains of the device. This has another wire to a microphone.

For a child who is getting no information about sound through hearing aids, a cochlear implant might be considered. I asked the mother of a totally deaf child if she had thought about a cochlear implant for her child. She said she certainly had, but it was not an option right now because the child was speaking and functioning well without it.

Most people who have received a cochlear implant have been helped by it. Some recipients have had success beyond anyone's wildest dreams, to the point that some speech can be understood without the additional support of speechreading. So far, the greatest benefit seems to be to individuals whose deafness occured after they developed language.

There are cochlear implant programs at various hospitals. A good cochlear implant program should be strong in three areas: testing for candidacy, surgery, and follow-up rehabilitation. There is a Cochlear Hotline, based in Colorado which provides people with information on the facilities nearest to their homes that handle cochlear implants. To contact the Cochlear Hotline, see the following information:

Cochlear Hotline
61 Inverness Drive East, Suite 200, Englewood, CO 80112
Telephone: Voice, (800) 458-4999; TTY, (800) 483-3123.

FM (Frequency-Modulation) Hearing Aid

BTE hearing aids become increasingly less effective as the distance between child and the speaker increases, beginning at six inches. The purpose of an FM hearing aid is to "collect" speech sounds at the source and transmit those sounds across a room to the child using FM technology without the waning caused by distance. FM hearing aids consist of two units, a radio receiver worn by the child and a radio transmitter worn by the parent or teacher or caregiver or sibling. Each unit is slightly smaller than a Sony Walkman. The units are recharged at night.

The child wears the FM receiver on a belt around his waist or a harness on his chest. There are cords which connect to boots which attach to the bottom of the child's hearing aids. The audiologist should order the personal hearing aid casings to have FM adapters. Some FMs have Off/On switches on the boots to control the child's environmental mikes. The child can run the cords under clothing to keep them from snagging. Some FM's have a loop of wire which goes around the user's neck. The quality of sound received is sometimes not as good as it is with a loop. It depends on the personal hearing aid's telecoil.

The parent or teacher wears the FM transmitter, a box the same size as the receiver with a plug-in microphone. The microphone is clipped on a lapel. Because noise from the wire rubbing on clothing is noticeable the unit should be clipped in place before it is turned on. The adult should perform the Ling Five-Sounds Test, (See Chapter 7) every time the unit is reconnected. The transmitter has an Off/On switch and can be turned off when the adult is talking to someone else privately. The standing joke about FMs is teachers forget they are turned on when they go to the bathroom.

Our audiologist showed us the latest in FMs at our last appointment. The whole unit is built in a hearing aid casing, with a small antenna at the back of the ear. It is a little bigger than an ordinary hearing aid, but much smaller than the FM box.

Hearing aids provide the maximum hearing possible at a close range. When the child is little, it is easy and normal for the mother to stay close to the child. As the child begins to walk, he begins to walk away from her voice. One week later he is running. The parent must move with the child to maintain good auditory input. An FM allows the parent not to have to physically keep up with a two- or-three-year-old, yet still able to talk to the child.

I exhausted myself running after Reid, making sure that he could hear every word I said. The audiologist said, "An FM might be a good idea

a. Free Ear FM System

b. Free Ear BTE FM System

c. User Changeable RO

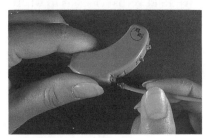

d. User Changeable Antenna

Figure 9.7 FM System
Photos courtesy of Phonic Ear

in school." Experts were beginning to realize **earshot** (See Chapter 13) applied to any child wearing hearing aids. I asked, "How about at home?" "There really is no need." If I lived with Reid as a preschooler again, I would use an FM while he was playing, in the car, and in shopping centers. That child has caused me so much grief by running off, curious about what was on the next counter. Once a hard-of-hearing child is ten feet away in a store, he is gone. You cannot get him back by standing and shouting louder than anyone else in the world, because he cannot hear you.

The child with an FM is identified as hard of hearing because he is wearing a box, which makes the parents visibly "the parents of a hard-of-hearing child." Our itinerant teacher of the deaf feared an FM might interfere with the special closeness a hard-of-hearing child develops with his parents, because it allows the child to be physically further away. However, she got to go home without Reid, every time she came to visit. She did not have to push herself, all the time to keep up with him as I did. Someone suggested to me that Reid might not develop the best speechreading skills if he depended too much on amplified hearing. I thought the child would spend more time hearing clearly which could be added to the speechreading experience.

Reid's FM was prescribed for him the year before school started. This allowed the school board the opportunity to batch-order FMs needed for the next year. We had Reid try out the unit a few times. He thought it was great playing auditory hide-and-seek with his siblings. Someone would take the microphone unit and hide somewhere in the house, then give Reid verbal clues as to where his brother or sister was hidden. Reid had to find the hiding place.

At a **VOICE for Hearing-Impaired Children** parent-sharing session, mothers discussing the use of FMs in school concluded that FM's raised **C**s to **B**s and **B**s to **A**s. Some children were going through the stage of refusing to wear their hearing aids, not using their FMs, to be like every one else. The parents allowed the children to experiment. Their marks

Figure 9.8 Reid Wearing FM in Kindergarten.
Photo by PAM Candlish

fell. Many of the children decided to use the FMs again, perhaps more enthusiastically because it was their choice and not their parents'. These children are mostly teenagers and old enough to choose.

Infrared Systems

All large public areas such as movie houses, theaters, town halls, churches, universities, and schools could have infrared systems installed. A transmitter broadcasts "the show." The infrared receiver is a pocket-sized box, battery-supported, with cords ending in a plastic silhouette of the hearing aid. The user puts the silhouette between his head and the hearing aid, turns the hearing aid to **T** and adjusts the volume on his hearing aid to hear what is being broadcast on the infrared system. The Sennheiser unit I used at Stratford, Canada has a receiver with a loudness dial hanging on two earphones. People who wear hearing aids take them out to use this unit. It is a real pleasure for me to hear speech clearly in a Shakespearean play again.

Public Communication Technology

When the hearing world and the Deaf Community must communicate there are technologies and skills available. At a meeting I attended for parents, students, and the community at a school for the Deaf, all stops were pulled, so nobody would feel left out. The school had FMs with neck loops for anyone to borrow. There was a public address system for people to speak. The FMs were hooked into the public address system. There were manual interpreters for every speaker and oral interpreters for signed presentations and **Real Time Captioning. Real Time Captioning** has a technician, much like a court stenographer who takes down every word spoken, which gets projected on an overhead screen. It is so fast that as a speaker, I was able to turn around and see what I had just said.

Oral Interpreters

Oral interpreters are people who are trained to silently repeat what the speaker has just said to convey an accurate message to the lipreader.

According to Diane L. Castle, formerly of the National Technical Institute for the Deaf, in Rochester, N.Y., oral interpreters use expression and natural gestures to convey the mood and intent of a message. Oral interpreters can be helpful in classrooms, at work, at meetings, and in other group situations where accurate lipreading is not possible because of distance, number of people, and speakers who can't be lipread.

Closed Captioning

Closed captioning which provides visual text for television shows, is a very desirable option as the child becomes literate. Fighting to understand every word said in a TV show or movie is exhausting. A closed captioner is usually tax deductible and a worthwhile investment if your child has difficulty following favorite TV shows. It might encourage the reading skills of other children in the house too. Many TVs have built-in captioners. When looking for a new set, ask for one of these.

Soundfield Amplification

A new technology has been developed to improve classrooms for all children using an FM microphone on the teacher and wall or ceiling-mounted loud speakers in the classroom. This provides a better acoustic environment by improving the ratio between the background noise and the teacher's voice. (also called the S/N or signal-to-noise ratio) Although it is better than a bare classroom, soundfield amplification is not as effective as personal FM units for hard-of-hearing children.

Telephone Device for the Deaf-TTY

A TTY is an evolution of a teletype message machine used heavily by businesses before the days of FAX and modem connection between computers. People with hearing problems can type messages to each other and have conversations. Local calls are the same as any other telephone charges. The US and Canadian telephone companies offer a reduced-rate on all long distance charges to registered TTY users. The cost of the message depends on the speed and skill of the people using the device.

Telephone Relay Service

People wishing to call people with speech or hearing difficulties who use a TTY also may place calls with the assistance of the Relay Service Operator. Look in your telephone book for your local services.

How Much is that Hearing Aid in the Window . . . The One with the Wagging Tail?

Imagine this: a pair of reliable, excellent ears on four active legs and with a happily wagging tail! Hearing-Ear dogs are hard at work all over the world "listening" for their hard-of-hearing owners. If you are a hard-of-hearing or deaf adult capable of looking after the needs of a dog and willing to learn to work with a Hearing Ear dog, you may qualify for a fully trained service dog. Hearing Ear dogs learn: basic obedience, good house manners; basic sign language commands; to respond to a door knock or bell, phone, timer, smoke detector, whistling kettle, and name calling. Most of the dog's work is done in the home and/or workplace. Hearing Ear dog rights are protected by law. They are allowed access to hotels, restaurants, schools and self-contained housing units. Many dogs accompany their masters to work, or to school, fly to holiday destinations and relax in the best hotels.
Patricia Taylor of *Hearing Ear Dogs of Canada.*

Children are not usually considered as applicants for Hearing Ear dogs. However, there have been some exceptions. The parents might have to care for the dog or share the care. Helping to look after the dog would benefit the child, as owning a pet benefits any child. Hearing-Ear dogs are working dogs. A child with hearing problems might feel **privileged** not **handicapped** to have such a special, clever pet.

For further information contact:

Hearing Dog Resource Center
P.O. Box 1080, Renton, WA. U.S. 98857-1080
Telephone: Voice and TTY, (1-800) 869-6898

Lions Foundation-Hearing Ear Dogs of Canada,
P.O. Box 907, Oakville, Ontario CANADA L6J 5E8
Telephone: Voice, (905) 842-2891; TTY, (905) 842-1585;
Fax, (905) 842-3373

Chapter 10
Smile Though
Your Heart is Breaking:
Buying and Inserting the
Hearing Aids and Meeting the Costs

United States Income Tax Deductions[1]

According to the Family Resource Center on Disabilities (20 East Jackson Boulevard, Room 900, Chicago, Illinois 60604, Telephone: 312-939-3513), as a parent of a disabled child you are entitled to income tax deductions for "medical expenses" covering the costs of:

1. Educational services (special instruction or training such as lipreading, sign language, speech instruction, auditory-verbal therapy);

---

[1]For Canadian Tax Deductions, see **Useful Tips and Thoughts 10** (p. 231) on Meeting the Costs of Hearing Problems.

2. Equipment and supplies (hearing aids, telephone/teletype equipment and repair and television adapter for closed captions);
3. Hospital services: laboratory exams and tests, medical treatments, medicines and drugs;
4. Professional services including speech therapist and psychologist;
5. Transportation (child and self to and from special schools and institutions, hospitals and clinics, doctors offices and pharmacists), and;
6. Service dog expenses for deaf persons.

If this exceeds 7.5 percent of your adjusted gross income.

It is important to document all your medical expenses by keeping careful records of all expenses with receipts, date of expense etc. for five years. Obtain certification from your doctor that the expense has been made for one or more of the following: diagnosis, cure, alleviation, prevention, treatment or dysfunction of your child's condition.

For more information, contact your local Internal Revenue Service, Information Service phone:1-800/829-1040.

Private speech pathologists, audiologists, and auditory-verbal therapists cost fifty to one hundred dollars an hour. Parents must pay for everything themselves, unless they have an extremely generous health insurance plan. Many health insurance plans in the United States do not pay for the remediation of hearing problems unless it can be proved that a delay in diagnosis resulted in a more serious problem.

It is hard to comprehend how important it is to get hearing aids onto the child, especially when you need every cent for food. If you cannot afford to buy the hearing aids, ask the audiologist if she knows of any charitable or service organization which might help you out. Some charities might be willing to sponsor your child, on an individual basis, for a short or extended period of time. If you receive help, be sure to write a "Thank You." Grandpa paid for our share of the hearing aids and both godparents sent money for earmolds.

Lots of people make their living dealing with your child's hearing problems. They have a right to be paid for what they do, but your child must not suffer if you do not have any money. Anyone that you come in contact with, will assume you are financially all right unless you tell them otherwise.

Earmolds and Getting the Hearing Aids

The materials used to make earmolds are being improved all the time, as a result of research by the large mold makers. Earmolds are expensive. Nobody can make them with the same physical characteristics for much less than the mold maker does. My husband suggests, "Earmolds on hearing aids are like tires on a car. Go for the best." Plastic impressions of the ear canal can be sent through the mail to a mold maker from anywhere in the world.

Either the hearing aid dealer or the audiologist will look in each ear to be sure that there is no accumulation of wax, or anything else. Then he will make impressions of the child's outer ear and ear canals to go to the mold maker. He will order the hearing aids from the manufacturer, and when the hearing aids come in and the earmolds are back, he will call and set up an appointment. Try to book it when the child is not hungry or tired. The professional will have done a final check on the new hearing aids in an electroacoustic testing box, to be sure that the factory did a good job.

He will show you each and every feature of the hearing aid and teach you minor trouble shooting techniques. You will listen to the aid with a stethoscope. Get your own stethoscope to use at home. Listen carefully to background noise, to someone talking about four feet away and to yourself saying **ah ee ou sh ss**. Become absolutely familiar with the hearing aids before you go home. The professional has the knowledge you need to keep the hearing aids running at optimum functioning.

Both parents, and the babysitter (if that is a full-time placement for the child) should go along for this fitting so that you will not have to start teaching spouse and sitter the minute you get home. Absolute knowledge passed along first hand from an expert is better than the confused instructions you might try to issue while you learn to live with hearing aids.

Before leaving the hearing aid dealer or audiologist, make sure you have as much information about the hearing aids as you can handle right

A standard earmold, from the inside.
Photo by Pat McMullon

A tragus earmold, used for greater losses to prevent feedback.
The top point of the mold extends right up into the corner of the ear.
Photo by Pat McMullon

An earmold for a three-week baby.
Courtesy of Ian MacIntosh, Ear Mold Design Ltd.
Photo by PAM Candlish

Figure 10.1 Earmolds.

now. Pick up several business cards and put them in your wallet, in your
telephone book, and in the hearing aid bag. You will need a receipt to
claim the hearing aid cost on your income tax. The professional will
give you warranty cards.

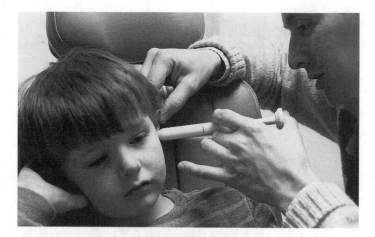

A large syringe is used to put impression material into the ear.
Photo by PAM Candlish

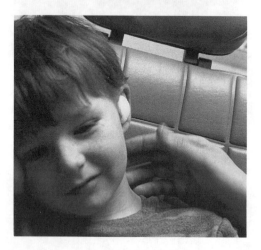

Then we must sit around with bated breath waiting for
the material to harden.
Photo by PAM Candlish

Figure 10.2 Making Impressions.

If your child's hearing aids are to be fine tuned with in-the-ear probe-microphone testing, the order of events changes. The child goes to the audiologist for an unaided-threshold hearing test. The audiologist will write the prescription for earmolds. The earmolds will be made, then the child goes back to the audiologist for further selection of hearing aids and probe-microphone testing with the earmolds.

How to Put in the Earmolds

It takes two hands and your full attention to put a hearing aid earmold into an ear. At first you might feel anxious and awkward. If you pull too hard on the child's ear, he might cry. Applying force to get the earmold in can hurt. But . . . the earmolds are custom designed for your child's individual ears and they do fit in there somehow, without using either a vise or a hammer because they went in, tickety boom, for the hearing aid dealer. If you relax, it will be easier.

Get the child's head at a comfortable height for you. Put the baby in the baby lounger on a table or counter. An older child can sit or stand so you do not have to bend. By the time you have put the hearing aids in one hundred times, you can do it hanging from the chandelier. Putting in the earmolds will become a motion as automatic as doing up a snowsuit.

Most human ears are variations on a basic shape, more or less straight at the front and round at the back. The earmold will be straight at the front, with a pointed "hook" at the top on the front, and curved at the back. Feel how soft and pliable the silicone earmold is.

Warning: The more you mangle the plastic tube coming out of the earmold, the more you will be driving to the hearing aid dealer to get it fixed. You cannot stick the tube back in with glue, because you might block the tube inside. Maneuver the earmold with your fingers, rather than twisting on the tube. When you are holding the earmold correctly, you can move your wrist up and down, or around in circles, without dropping the earmold.

To put the earmold into the child's ear, with one hand, pull the child's ear (lobe or pinna [top of the outer ear], depending on age), just a tiny bit to straighten the ear canal. Use the rest of your fingers as a "support" to control head movement. With the other hand put the earmold into the child's ear canal, about one-eighth turn backwards, and rotate your hand forward to catch the hook under the top front of the ear. If the hook is not caught properly, the earmolds will feed back and fall out.

Make sure the earmold is seated as far into the ear as it can go, push firmly on the earmold right over the part that goes into the ear canal. Hang the hearing aid on the child's ear, adjusting it slightly at the hook

Putting in the hearing aids should always be a happy time.
Photo by Pat McMullon

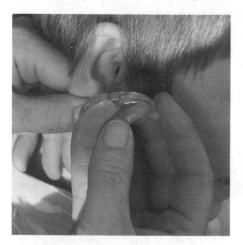 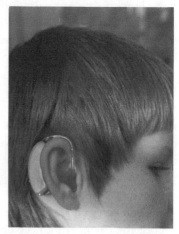

Gently pull the child's outer ear to straighten the ear canal,
hold earmold rather than tubing and insert in the ear, rotating until the
earmold is properly set.
Photo by Pat McMullon

Figure 10.3 Putting in the Earmolds.

to angle snugly into the head. Check the volume setting and turn the
switch to M for microphone. Do the Ling Five-Sounds test. Be sure the
child hears the range of the five sounds: **ah, ee, ou, sh, ss.**

With infants, putting the earmolds on can be intense business. Smile, even if you feel like crying. Your child is not stupid. He will pick up his basic attitude about putting on the hearing aids from you. A smile will reassure the child that this is o.k.. Smile a lot while the child is having his hearing aids put on and while he is wearing them. Have listening activities ready to make listening fun as soon as the hearing aids are turned on. Reward your spouse when he or she installs the earmolds independently.

The baby or child will probably take the hearing aids out by pulling on the plastic tubing. This is going to happen all the time so you have to hope the tubes can take it. When you take the hearing aids out, unhook the earmold at the top of the ear before pulling on the plastic tubes. The earmold has to rotate enough to unhook at the top and will easily pop out after that.

Reid could take his hearing aids out within twenty-four hours of getting them when he was a baby. Then we had to put the hearing aids back in, again and again all day long. When I was too stressed trying to keep the hearing aids in his ears we would call it quits for the day.

There are several theories on how to get the child to leave the hearing aids in his or her ears. There is the intellectual approach where the parent talks about how great the hearing aids are. You have to believe in this one to get it to work, unless your child is enraptured by the hearing aids right from the beginning. There are the ingenious physical approaches: little rolls of adhesive tape between the child's scalp and the hearing aid—double-sided extra-strong surgical adhesive tape works too; **bonnets or headbands reduce the effectiveness of the hearing aids if the hearing aids are covered by material**. There are "Kiddihooks," which make it harder for the child to get the hearing aids off. We found that the more involved the gimmicks became, the more Reid would find to pull on, and the longer it took each time to put the hearing aids back in his ears.

I made a hearing aid harness, similar to a reading glasses holder from a light grade of decorative cording. We had a whole set in colors to match his T-shirts. The harness had a loop at each end which attached to the hooks of the hearing aids and was safety pinned to his shirt at the back of his neck. This kept Reid from throwing away the hearing aids after he took them out, until he learned to take everything apart.

Many parents make this harness with dental floss. Floss is strong and thin which makes it harder for the child to pull out the hearing aids by pulling on the harness.

Many children are perfectly happy to wear their hearing aids right from the start. I had so much trouble getting Reid to wear them, that I almost did not believe any other type of behavior was possible. Reid was stubborn and opinionated for two years and continued to vent his grievances with me on the hearing aids until he was past four. Dr. Ling says a continually stubborn child is usually a sign of inappropriate aiding. Reid's good ear was aided first, while we cleared up otitis media in his other ear. Before his second birthday, Reid would take his hearing aid out of his better ear and put it in his other ear. He was telling us we had the wrong ear and showing he was aware that the hearing aid could make it better.

Reid learned to put the earmolds in himself in kindergarten. At home, he figured Mummy or Daddy were the best people to do the job. At school, he knew more than anyone else, so he just started to do it for himself. One night he showed me he could put one hearing aid in. We told everybody in the house and there were cheers. The next morning he did not feel capable. After a couple of days, he announced he would put one hearing aid in. I reviewed a few pointers with him, showed him a reasonable way to push the hearing aid with one finger, and had him feel the hole in his ear with that finger, and showed him the part of the earmold that went in the hole. Fortunately, the earmold went in, tickety boom, and he felt confident enough to try the other one. Again there was riotous praise for success. The next morning he demurred, but my husband and I both said, "But you did it last night, no problem" and the rest of the family chorused, "No problem" à la Alf. Reid did it all by himself.

Earmolds made of ultrasoft silicone are difficult to get into the ear without plenty of lubrication. We use a drop of Vitamin E oil per earmold. Mineral oil, which was used on his first earmolds, will eat the new earmold material. Avoid using Vaseline, or mineral oil. K-Y jelly might work, but Vitamin E oil has a healing quality as well.

The child should learn to put his hearing aids in without a mirror, so he can handle them anywhere, any place, any time, even in the dark. We checked Microphone/Off position, and the volume control because he was not wildly accurate at age six. A child at the age of reason, somewhere around four, can be talked into inserting his own hearing aids, providing he can understand you, right from diagnosis. Before instructing the child, try to put one in your ear.

I hope that we are not going to get too many more children diagnosed as late as Reid was. I hope parents will be putting earmolds into tiny babies' ears, if it has to be. If I could do again anything in my life it would be to get Reid aided as an infant. So if you have a tiny baby on whom to put hearing aids, try and be grateful. Scientists are beginning to understand how important hearing is during the first six months of life. The sooner a hard-of-hearing baby is aided, the sooner he can put **ah** and **ou** together.

Left and right hearing aids and left and right earmolds seem to become indistinguishable after you take them apart to clean them. If your hearing aid dealer has not already done so, use a stylus or knife point to scratch **L** on the hearing aid for the left ear, and **R** on the hearing aid for the right ear. The tuning of the hearing aids is done specifically for each ear. It can be impossible to tell which hearing aid belongs in which ear if you have not marked them. I always tried to put Reid's hearing aids down on the table as they would be in his ears. He had two different numbers and sizes of hearing aids. After getting confused a number of times and having to find the prescribing audiogram to find out whether the 820 went in his left ear or right, we marked the casings. Life was easier after that.

With practice, you can learn to tell left and right earmolds, because the flat side of the earmold is the front. It is simpler to mark each earmold with an indelible pen, in the beginning anyway. Put an initial on the casing of the hearing aid in case the child gets together with another child wearing the same hearing aids.

Maybe we would have more fun with our hearing aids if we were to decorate them or keep them trendy with stickers. I put "Ghostbuster" stickers on Reid's FM. Why not on the hearing aids too? Why do we try to hide them, with flesh colored plastic? They could be pretty, or a statement of undying allegiance.

The barber cuts Reid's hair to hide the hearing aids. The hair hides the hearing aids, the hearings aids are not "invisible." Cathy had a little girl with beautiful long curly hair. Cathy felt how she arranged her child's hair showed how she was feeling about the hearing aids that morning. Some days she wanted to hide them and some mornings she wished they were "day-glo red" and screaming out the message, "This child wears hearing aids." Cathy felt people were more inclined to make special considerations when the hearing aids were obvious. When the child's hair hid the hearing aids, she became a very pretty, but for some unknown reason, badly behaved, unresponsive child.

The child and the parent have to have a basic understanding of the joy of listening, and the freedom which hearing aids give. Every child has his own personality and will figure out his own philosophy. Driving home after buying Reid new hearing aids just before his fifth birthday, I almost went off the road because a little voice said, "Thank you Mummy, for buying me new hearing aids." He was being polite, but it did not fit into his normal behavior and knocked me for a loop. It was quiet, unexpected, and really quite grown-up. I did not tell him the things going through my mind. I said, "You are welcome, Reid. Anytime."

Chapter 11
Batteries: Life and Death
for the Hearing Aids
and the Child

Most hearing aid dealers have reasonable prices for batteries and a vested interest in keeping the supply fresh. Drug stores and department stores have batteries if you get caught short. Camera stores have batteries which they sell for five dollars a battery. Keep the receipts for all hearing aid battery purchases for income tax purposes. We keep a battery supply in each car, in my purse, in the office at school and in the hearing aid bag.

Mercury batteries lose power just sitting around. The latest batteries on the market are zinc air cells which have a paper pull tab on one side. Removing the tab reveals two little holes which allows air into the battery. Until the tab is removed the batteries do not deteriorate. This means they can be stored longer. We have found that zinc air batteries are almost twice as expensive as the mercury batteries, but they last longer.

There is a difference in the output of the batteries. Mercury batteries have a higher output at the beginning of use, while zinc air batteries have a lower, more constant level of power. To a certain point it is a consumer's decision on which type of battery to buy. However, some hearing aids do better with fresh mercury batteries. If the audiologist recommends a certain type of battery, use her advice.

In the good old days we threw out the dead batteries, but they can be recycled either at the hearing aid dealer or at a camera store. Make sure you keep dead batteries in an inaccessible place until you get rid of them. And don't get the batteries to be recycled mixed up with the new batteries.

Our hearing aid dealer has a new battery tester on his counter, which is a little piece of metal attached to a voltmeter. The battery sits on the metal and a wand is touched to the battery. The power potential of the battery shows on the voltmeter. Over the years we have encountered many variations, most of which have provided endless challenge to decide whether it is the brand new battery from the new supply which is dead, or whether the battery tester is asleep.

The hearing aids will tell you whether a battery is alive or dead. If the sound is getting weak so is the battery. Throw out a weak battery. There is no point in saving money on batteries by using them to the last drop of power.

According to a customer service representative of Duracell, all hearing aid batteries are poisonous. One can kill a child. Spare batteries must be kept out of the child's reach. I always laugh when reading the warning on the package which says "**Keep Away from Children**." Who wears the hearing aids during early childhood? Batteries should never be changed in front of the young child. That seemed like good advice, so we followed it. At two-and-a-half, Reid could take the hearing aids completely apart, the earmolds off, the hooks off and the batteries out, in minutes. Usually he would throw them across the room, or down a heat duct, or into the sofa. When I could not find the second battery amongst all the pieces, I asked two-and-half-year-old Reid, "Where is the battery?" He pointed to his mouth, several times. I phoned the local hospital to say we were coming. The hospital phoned Poison Control and got the protocol:

1. Take an X-ray to verify battery whether a battery is in the digestive tract.
2. Transport patient to nearest hospital that has a scope, a surgeon, an X-ray machine, an anesthetist and an X-ray technician available.

Reid took one look at the X-ray machine and decided he would rather die than lie down there. We told him it was a camera to take his picture and he would have to say "cheese." He was not anywhere near understanding much speech, but he had said "tees" when a picture was taken, so Ross lay down on the X-ray table and said, "Cheese." Reid followed Ross' example and lay down and said "teez" too. The picture was snapped. There was the battery, shining like a moon through the murky shadows. The nearest hospital meeting the protocol equipment requirements was sixty miles away. Ross drove "firmly." A surgeon tickled Reid's tummy, viewed the X-ray and said we would have to wait several hours, then take another X-ray. If the battery was still in his stomach, he would be anesthetized and scoped to remove the battery.

The acid in the stomach is very strong. The seal on the battery will resist the stomach acid for a number of hours and then is likely to break, allowing the acid in the battery out into the child's stomach. The battery acid is stronger than stomach acid and will eat through the wall of the child's stomach. The child will bleed to death. The digestive acids beyond the stomach are not as strong as the acids in the stomach and will not melt the seal on the battery. If the battery passes from the stomach into the duodenum within a short period of time, the child will be all right.

Reid wandered around all the goodie machines in the emergency waiting room, begging for a "tok", "ba ba", even "wa", but the surgeon had said, "**Nothing by mouth**." Two hours passed and it was time for the next X-ray. When he saw the X-ray machine, he climbed up, lay down and said, "teez." The X-ray showed the battery had moved on to safety. We were sent home with a bottle of laxative to speed up the process. An X-ray the next day at our local hospital confirmed that it was gone.

The surgeon told us the emergency department saw eighty-four children (not all hard-of-hearing) with small batteries in their digestive tract the previous year. It was too easy for a child to take the battery out

Unitron has a tamper-resistant battery holder which requires the insertion of
a pointed object into the small opening in the battery holder.
Photo courtesy of Unitron

Phonic Ear also offers tamperproof battery clips which can be put on by hand,
but require a screwdriver or other small pointed tool to remove.

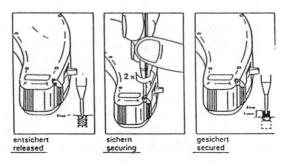

| entsichert released | sichern securing | gesichert secured |

Phonic Ear offers tamperproof battery doors for all mini-size hearing aids.
This is a kit which comes with a screwdriver to properly position
the screw safeguard.

Figure 11.1 Hearing Aid Battery Protectors.

of his hearing aid. I contacted a number of hearing aid companies and suggested a tiny screw through the battery drawer would save lives.

Unitron now has a tamperproof battery carrier. Instead of having a flange on the carrier to open it, there is a small hole into which a ball-point pen fits. It would require a great deal of fine motor control for a child to get this open. I don't think it would be fail-safe, but better than the flange on all of Reid's aids from the time he was a baby. **Phonic Ear** has two methods available to make the aids childproof. One is a screw holding the battery drawer shut, which has its own special screw driver to undo. The other is a metal clip which fits over the battery casing. If your child is under five, insist that his hearing aids be equipped with one of these devices.

Now that the hearing aid companies have begun to do something about the danger of the button batteries, you can have these modifications installed at the time you buy the aids. If you are "making do" with Great-Aunt Henny's hearing aid, you must have the battery drawer childproofed. We have acquired two hearing aids from deceased relatives, had them approved and tuned by the audiologist and use them for back-up hearing aids.

If you or the child's caretaker find the child has eaten a battery, go immediately to the hospital. The battery may pass through, but you have no way of knowing that. The alternative is a child who bleeds to death in a matter of minutes, while you watch helplessly.

Chapter 12
Ling and I

My daughter, Barbara, who has no hearing loss, had serious speech problems. At age two, she had cadence, rhythm and vowels, but no consonants, substituting 'h' instead. Barbara could follow intricate instructions from another room and a hearing loss was never a consideration, but she could not talk. Barbara was frustrated and demonstrating some autistic behaviors such as hand flapping, spinning things, and self-isolation. Ross and I did not know what to do, but we were sure we could do something.

Finally, the week of her third birthday we went to the speech pathologist for assessment. Halfway through testing the pathologist exclaimed, "This child has serious problems. She has had a year to habituate errors and will need work by you and me for years to undo the damage." Once a week, or once every two weeks, we went to the speech pathologist. Sound by sound, blend by blend, Barbara began to talk.

At the beginning, I did not know what we were doing, but was enthusiastic and unforgiving with Barbara. If she said a sound incorrectly that she had learned, she was made to say it properly. The form of her speech was constantly corrected, the content of her language was ignored. The message was never what she said, but how she said it. This led, I believe, to an inability to weigh what she was saying later on, to lie with utter innocence, confident she had said it right.

Barbara developed manipulative skills, we kept right on. Her ability to talk gave her the freedom to communicate. The autistic behavior stopped. By about age five-and-a-half, Barbara had perfect speech as long as she was not tired. As the day went by, her speech would slip. By bedtime we were back to "**h**" and vowels. Bedtime remained early for all the children, for Barbara's sake. By age seven, the "**h**s" were only there in times of extreme fatigue. At age ten, Barbara got an "A" on her speech at school about her very pink bedroom.

Looking back, I would pay as much attention to language content as to form, throughout the preschool years and relax about the goals of perfect speech. It is wrong to sit in a blue room and practice the word "red", but I did that with Barbara because I did not know any better.

Barbara's speech therapy taught me a lot about speech. Her speech pathologist (and my friend) Gay said, "God sent you Barbara and then he let you have Reid." I subscribe to the "raisin theory" myself, but it was an effective background to begin parenting a child with hearing problems. I knew each speech sound was different. I reasoned Reid could only produce the sounds he could hear. So all we had to do was find a chart of the speech sounds, circle the sounds Reid was making and we would know what he could hear.

I wanted a graph and letters sitting in one place. It was easy to find an audiogram with a "speech banana" placed on it, but it was of no use to me. At a publisher's clearance, for two dollars, I bought a book called *Your Deaf Child's Speech and Language* by Mary Courtman-Davies. There was a graph with speech sounds plotted on it. Ross and I listened to one-and-a-half-year-old Reid's screeches, circled the sounds and decided conclusively that he was hard of hearing. We became very concerned that we should do something immediately to help Reid learn how to talk, which was probably aggravated by how hard we had found the job of re-teaching Barbara to talk.

The public library had a tiny selection of books, mostly about signing, to help parents with deaf children. But there was one book which provided a key to the puzzle. *Aural Habilitation* (1978) by Dr. Agnes Ling Phillips and Dr. Daniel Ling is about getting the best amplification on a child and creating an "aural" environment in which the child can learn to listen.

The librarians got me books through inter-library loan. What I could not understand I passed over, with the assumption that it would come up again, explained by someone else and more understandable. Often the librarians or the preschool itinerant teacher would comment, "My! That seems awfully technical. Why don't you read this instead?" I read both.

Reid had one speech assessment at the provincial school for the Deaf. At chronological age twenty-four months, (how old he really was) his hearing age (the age by which most hearing children have developed a particular set of auditory skills) estimated at one-to-three months, (or how long the child had worn hearing aids), and his speech was assessed at the zero-to-six months level. The speech pathologist suggested that we regress his speech back to birth and begin again, just as though he were a brand new baby. She recommended speech pathology but not through her services because he was "not deaf enough."

At the hospital, we were on a waiting list for speech services for a slow-developing child, even before the diagnosis of hearing loss. The hospital ran early communication workshops for parents on the waiting list. We learned tricks of the trade like using a kleenex to show the difference between a voiced or voiceless sound. I had the only child with hearing problems. My problems seemed gargantuan.

We used some gestures because we felt Reid should not have to experience the same frustration that his sister had. When he used a gesture I would give him a sound or syllable such as **ba** for **bottle**, and a full sentence related to the gesture. He had gestures for **milk**, **peanut butter**, **cookie**, **cheese**, **no**, **stop**, **car**. As soon as he developed a sound related to the gesture we used the sound and dropped the gesture. At twenty-six months, Reid had a three word vocabulary **Ba-bottle**, **Wa-water** and **Ma-Mummy**.

The story of Helen Keller had been on TV and inspired the whole family. Reid had to tolerate being dragged over to the tap by his siblings and having his hand put in the water while the children said "**Wa Wa**".

I reminded the children that Reid could see. It was not going to be as hard a job as Annie Sullivan had. Sibling inspiration is everything. Reid produced, "**Wa Wa**." This was Reid's first use of connected speech sound, a double phoneme!

I spent hours reading anything and everything to Reid, but focused on a few suitable vocabulary books, with clear pictures on a plain background. Our first book had six pictures- a ball,a chair, a flower, car keys, milk, and a baby. It took three months to master six words and another month to master the next six. Progress seemed awfully slow. He was babbling and gurgling, but useful speech was emerging. Once in a long while, other people could understand it. Our itinerant teacher of the deaf was terrific at getting Reid to do things like cooperating with the hearing testing, and supporting me, but did not have the speech knowledge of "where do we go from here" that we needed.

It was just plain luck that Dan Ling was only one hundred miles away at the University of Western Ontario. We phoned for an appointment. Dan had a look at what we were doing with Reid. He talked to Reid and listened to him. He said Reid was coming along nicely and we were doing fine.

Ling put us in touch with an auditory-verbal therapist and told us about his seminar at the University of Western Ontario. I took his seminar on *Speech and the Hearing Impaired Child*, (1976) when Reid was three and again when Reid turned five, because it was based on his new book, *Foundations of Spoken Language for Hearing-Impaired Children*, (1989).

Beginning with vocalization and progressing through simple sounds to sentences, we used Dr. Ling's method with Reid. Several auditory-verbal therapists have told me Ling is used remedially and they rely on other programs. Ling does not present his system as a remedial system, but cautions non-intervention in a child's speech until the child is using speech. The beauty of the Ling method is knowing where the child is in the development of speech and language, and focusing on a limited number of targets for two-to-three minutes. The parent fills the child's ears with sound, listens to the child talk, and works on speech from time to time.

The Ling method is catchy and is said to be a drawing card in many programs. Further study will reveal nothing more than the Five-Sounds

Test used every morning. If you are going to use Ling's methods to teach your child, read his books yourself.

Several speech pathologists told me, "Simplify your speech. Your speech is too rich and varied for a hard-of-hearing child." Gay tells me what she said was, "Simplify your language. It is too complex for a hard-of-hearing child to imitate." Times change. Newer techniques have resulted in less rigid suggestions for children with speech and language difficulties. Tiffany was never exposed to baby talk, or simple sentences and learned to speak beautifully. I was ecstatic when Ling stated, "Simple speech teaches simple speech."

I have driven hundreds of miles to listen to Dr. Ling speak. He clarifies matters for a confused parent and never berates a parent for not knowing any better. Besides he can be funny. Dr. Ling was more accessible to us than the "established services for hard-of-hearing children." I incant the Ling Five-Sounds Test every night. I teach it to every person who can use it.

Daniel Ling's *Speech and the Hearing-Impaired Child*, (1978) provided, with a certain amount of difficulty, the basis of Reid's preschool speech program. The difficulties involved in using the book were because I did not have the basic knowledge to read a book written for other professionals in the field. This is often a problem faced by parents attempting to teach their child themselves. Attending the seminar made the information easier to understand.

Ling's *Foundations of Spoken Language for Hearing-Impaired Children*, (1989) carries speech training beyond phonemes and words and sentences. It incorporates both speech and language skills at the same time.

Chapter 13
Within Earshot:
Maximizing the Auditory
Environment and Other
Physical Considerations

A law of physics says the volume of sound decreases by six decibels for each doubling of distance from the source.

Distance from sound	Decibel Drop
three inches	6dB
six inches	12dB
twelve inches	18dB
two feet	24dB
four feet	30dB
eight feet	36dB
sixteen feet	42dB

Earshot is the limit of the distance across which a sound can be heard. You must learn to talk to your child within earshot, otherwise only partial messages get through, less as the distance increases. Reid's range of earshot for his ear with a mild loss is four to six feet. Ask your audiologist for the exact range of earshot for your child. Train yourself to communicate with the child within earshot. Adapt your ways to the laws of physics and let it become second nature to move in closer before speaking.

Ling demonstrates earshot with a tape recorder and microphone. He speaks into the microphone at a distance of three inches, six inches, one foot, two feet, four feet, eight feet. At sixteen feet he shouts, then goes back to the microphone and whispers from three inches. The tape is replayed. Ling's voice fades as he moves away from the microphone. His shouting at sixteen feet is barely audible, compared to the clarity of the whisper at three inches.

If the child is two-and-a-half-feet tall and you are five feet tall, you have used up about two-and-a-half-feet of earshot, the distance from your mouth to the child's ears. Anything you say will be about twenty-six decibels quieter because the child is shorter. To compensate for this, get down to the child's level; squat, kneel, sit on the floor, or on a small sturdy chair. Lifting the child up gets tiring and is not recommended. Sitting the child on your knee is effective for reading books, either facing you so that he can lipread too, or facing away to enhance the use of his residual hearing.

Speaking from across a room is a waste of your energy unless you are clearly visible and the child lipreads. Many parents use a quiet voice or a whisper right at the hearing aid to speak to the child even in the midst of a birthday party. It is a hidden advantage we have, which parents of ordinary children do not, because they have never learned about earshot.

Never shout at the child from a distance. Shouting changes the form of the consonants and your message will be weak and garbled. If you shout in his hearing aid the child will not hear you either because the sound suppressors will block you out.

Built into just about every hearing aid is a sound suppressor which cuts out incoming sounds that will be too loud to go into the child's ears.

This protects his hearing from noisy things like other children, fire alarms and irate parents who have forgotten that they should never shout. It is a safety feature of the hearing aid, called the SSPL that sounds above a certain loudness are suppressed.

When the school bell rings, Reid just about jumps out of his skin in spite of the suppression circuit in his hearing aid. The noise is below his sound supressor level, but still very loud. A fire alarm is louder. He does not hear it because the circuit of his hearing aid has suppressed the noise. If he is on the other side of the room from the fire alarm he will hear the alarm until he is close enough to the sound that the sound suppressors block it out. Reid takes his hearing aids out in the presence of loud repetitive sound, almost before the sound suppressors work.

The child whispering, or speaking in a quiet voice will occlude other sounds coming in to the hearing aids. The child shouting and arguing or crying fills them with his own noises. Wait for a moment of quiet to get a word in edgewise. This makes it hard to comfort a hurt and crying child. Hug, stroke, and hold the child to calm him before re-establishing verbal contact. Use a visual contact. This can be so frustrating for parent and child when you have no idea of what the problem is.

When Reid has a temper tantrum, he fires his hearing aids across the room. Being a normal person, I interpret this as despicable, disagreeable behavior and get even crosser, because he's doing it to get me. But . . . as an intelligent, rational mother of a child not presently engaged in a tantrum, I can tell you why. I think that he can't stand to listen to himself. A child's screams go into the hearing aids and come out at maximum levels. You cannot punish the child because he fired his hearing aids across the room in the heat of passion. You would too. Get the hearing aids before he throws them. Sometimes, living with a hard-of-hearing child is pretty intense. This is one of those times.

Earshot applies to any sound source, not just live voices. The acoustical suspension speakers to my sound system are installed in the corners of the family room at the ceiling. Reid paid no attention to any music until we were playing a new CD of *Tubular Bells* very loudly. Three-year-old Reid started to boogie, in perfect time to the music. The music got quieter, still audible to the rest of us, but Reid threw himself on the floor shouting, "Put dah moosic back. I like dat moosic. Put it back." We figured his hearing aids had juiced out and rushed to change them.

He put his hands over his ears and said, "Hit not mah hrung aid. Mah hrung aid is fine. It de moosic. It topped. Put it back." We put the CD back to the beginning, but the moment had passed. The speakers are too far away for Reid to hear moderately loud music. Unless it is too loud for the rest of us, he does not hear it.

Earshot applies to the TV. Reid has his favorite place to sit, two-and-a-half-feet from the TV. If his space is occupied by man or beast, he will sit on top of them, stand in front of them blocking the entire screen, or go and do something else. He cannot hear the TV properly from any other spot in the room.

School plays and concerts present another challenge. The little kids on stage do not project well, the seats are flat. Two of the children will be in one concert, one at the beginning and one at the end, so I can neither sneak in late nor leave early. The siblings want father, mother and other siblings to enjoy an occasion into which they have put so much work. Reid can see little, hear nothing and finds the minutes long. A whole roll of lifesavers (they do not make much sound) does not keep him amused. He starts to scrape the chairs, check out the neighbors, crawl down the rows, pleads a bathroom trip, thumps his feet, kicks me, and looks for anything of more interest. The concert goes on and on. The room is full of parents and siblings and even hearing children have their tolerances for this sort of thing. Finally my child gets up on stage and Reid falls asleep. Acoustically it is a nightmare which can lead to behavior problems. In some ways it is ridiculous that we try to take him, but this school was going to be his kindergarten.

It is necessary to use some gestures or hand signals to compensate for distance. I still use two gestures, a quiet "No" and an imperative "Stop that at once". Once while Reid was having impressions made and about to pull on the string, I signed, "Stop that at once." The audiologist looked at me aghast, "You do not use sign language with this child, do you?" I said, "No, but there are times when a few words come in handy, like the moment when his ears are full of plastic and he cannot hear."

Parents are responsible for the child's safety first and his speech second. There are many times in the day when he is out of earshot, out of reach, and still must be stopped. Shouting does not work, even though it is a natural inclination. From ten feet he is deaf. In dangerous situations, no one should ever rely on, "He seems to hear me okay," but should move within earshot, use the FM if it is on, use some sort of gesture, or run and grab the child which is just another gesture to compensate for lack of hearing.

Sometimes, if the environment is quiet, Reid can hear from twenty feet but his processing time is extended. (Processing time is the time it takes for a message to be heard and understood.) At school a teacher talked to him while he was putting on his coat. He responded to her questions with about 75 percent accuracy and with a significant delay. An uninformed person would say "That child does not really have a hearing problem." The processing time shows that he did not hear well, but is coping. Unfortunately, extended processing time makes the child look stupid. Reid appeared to be unable to remember the classroom visitor which was a six-foot tooth.

The parents must train themselves to be within earshot. The hearing world must be taught that hearing aids make it better, but not best and to move in closer. When the child is out of earshot it is necessary to compensate either by getting into the child's earshot by moving faster than the child is going, to plan in advance and use an FM, or to use some sort of gesture. There is no magic about it, out of earshot means "hearing-closed."

Our houses are noisy. Each appliance does its job and makes noise. Our refrigerator began life on a crooked floor and has to be "levelled" or it grinds, whirs and rattles. Sometimes it is necessary to unplug the fridge until we have finished whatever we are doing near it. The teacher of the deaf pointed out how loud the fridge was. We lived with it and never heard it.

Air conditioners and fans often make noise. The silent ceiling fan in our kitchen creates enough wind that Reid can hear nothing but wind noise when it is on. We have had conversations which ended with Reid continuing to do something when he has been told to stop. It took a while to figure out it was the fan's wind, not the child's apparent willfulness. Computers can be another source of obliterating noise, especially printers.

At home we have hundreds of little routines and controls that make the passage of each day easier, beginning with our own spatial determination of earshot. If Reid is watching TV, without thinking about it, I walk to the end of the sofa to speak to him. Practice has taught my body to always do this, so I am sure he can hear me. In a strange house the earshot considerations are different and ambient noise levels are confusing both for Reid and me.

When Reid was little we worked hard to maximize his auditory environment. We were told to get rid of the unnecessary sounds in the house so Reid could concentrate on developing his speech. This was all very well, but I resented not having Beethoven, Brahms and the Beatles floating around the house. Finding out that Reid did not hear music any less than fairly loud, unless he was hooked up to the sound system, meant that I could play it at a level he does not hear without interfering with his speech and language development.

So that Reid could enjoy music too, we decided to bypass the hearing aids and find high-output headphones with individual volume controls for each ear. At their Canadian headquarters in Burlington, Canada, KOSS, a leading manufacturer of electronics, adapted our SST/60 headphones by adding individual volume controls, after I explained the problem with the different hearing levels in Reid's ears. Reid now has music in both ears. I turn the volumes completely down, he puts on the headphones and adjusts the volume for each ear. The sound systems most of us have in our houses today can be modified to give the pleasure of music to just about every hard-of-hearing child. There are amplifiers with sixteen-band graphic equalizers, which allow you to 'paint' the child's hearing loss right into the sound mix. The loudness of music must never be allowed to reach the hearing aid's suppression circuit level. This should be pointed out to the sound salesperson, who is usually deafened from working with sounds at 140 decibels at rock concerts. If you can afford this option, then a higher quality of music is possible. If you cannot, then a monaural patch cord through the aids is better than nothing and only costs about eight dollars. Reid has his own CDs. What joy I have when he asks to listen to *Petah and the Woof*, just as other children want to hear their favorite CDs.

With four children, two dogs, a cat, a bird, a turtle (hibernating or dead) and a fish, it is reasonable to expect the house to be finished in a way that makes it easy to clean. I like shiny white walls, bare wood floors and a minimum of things to clean. Unfortunately, the easier it is to clean, the less sound absorption there is in the material and the more sounds will bounce around from walls to ceiling to floors. Corduroy, velvets, wall-to-wall carpeting, acoustic tile on the ceiling and generous drapes make a better acoustic environment. Acoustic tile ceilings are better than plaster, but ugly to me. I "hang" expanded vinyl wallpaper on the ceilings, with enough rise in the patterns to stop the sounds from bouncing back. It does not do much, but is better than a hard, smooth surface. Papering a ceiling is a matter of timing, aim, and a few expletives.

When you are contemplating redecorating, try to do the room where the hard-of-hearing child spends the most time with an eye to sound absorption. This will make listening easier for the child. Also it will make life nicer for the other people living with the hard-of-hearing child, who can be very noisy when playing. A large corduroy tablecloth draped over a little table masks noise from thumping toys on hard tables and becomes a neat tent too.

At the Science Center in Toronto there is a tunnel built with total sound-absorption technology, using foam and perforated metal. While admiring the engineering of sound baffles, you can listen to yourself do things like click your fingers or speak, crumple paper or plastic bags, and scuff your feet. Each sound is clear, unmuffled by other sounds of our world. The audiologist's "cave" is engineered the same way. While you are not aiming for eight inches of foam on your walls, you will understand more about maximizing the auditory environment through use of sound absorbers rather than hard reflectors, after you have experienced the extremes. Perhaps your audiologist can book an extra fifteen minutes and give you some time to play and learn about sounds in her testing room.

We created a good auditory environment for Reid when he was little. He did not go to nursery school where he would have been exposed to background noise. The public school is very noisy compared to our home so we added background noise when he was four. I worked with him near the TV for visual and auditory distraction, reading or talking about anything that was not on TV. Sometimes it was too much, and the TV won, and sometimes I was more fascinating, but he learned to cope with a variety of sounds and not just my voice in a perfect environment. This is particularly important for a child with a mild or moderate loss who is bombarded with inconsistent background noise. That is the reason for using FMs on any child who wears hearing aids. There are applications in the classroom for FMs even on unaided children, either to compensate for a mild loss which does not need hearing aids, or to shut out the distractions of the classroom for a child with auditory processing problems, but no hearing loss.

You must evaluate any environment in which your child spends a lot of time, from day care to the playroom. If the walls, ceilings and floors are hard, you have to question what benefit the child is getting. If a child learns to spend hours in an acoustically awful environment by not listening, you are wasting valuable language-learning time. If the child is in an auditory-verbal program at home and doing reasonably well, then goes out to a noisy nursery school and starts coping more visually or withdrawing, the benefit of peer language is being lost to awful acoustics. The child can develop his own coping techniques such as moving closer to the speaker during the weekly story hour at the library; that is reasonable coping. The child is not being stressed for long periods of time. If the child is in the same place, his playroom or a day care room, for two hours every morning, optimal language-learning time, you have to change the acoustics of the room or request that it be done.

A large rug can make a church basement better, as can piles of stuffed animals and some heavy drapes. You have to be involved long-term to get the acoustics improved for your child. However, there usually is no objection if you bring your own rug and leave it there. Buy a large bound-on-all sides remnant of broadloom at a rug store.

Most schools have fireproofing regulations regarding rugs and carpets. Some schools will buy a "flying carpet" to go under the hard-of-hearing child's desk and his neighbors'. The carpet moves up the grades with the child. You may have to work through the Special Education department. Eventually the teachers will learn the children are a little bit easier with a rug under them, but currently this is an area where parental insistence usually wins. School janitors hate rugs because they are sixteen times as much work, so say thank you to the janitor for his extra work.

There is little you can do to improve the noise in the family car. Driving at highway speed in my Honda Civic, is an experience of 90 to 100 decibels of wind and road noise, even with the windows shut. Driving in my father-in-law's luxury executive living room on wheels is an experience as to how quiet a car can be made. I could not afford to feed my in-laws' car, let alone buy it. Reid does not hear in our car.

If only he would wear his seat belt. That has been a battle for years. When the hard-of-hearing child is in the back seat, he cannot hear you saying, "do up your seat belt." I tried stopping the car and refusing to drive until the seat belt was done up. Reid was content to sit by the side of the road for ever. I have talked with him. I have taken him to visit the police. It is dangerous to turn around to communicate with the child while driving the car. It is even more dangerous to take both hands off the steering wheel and resort to sign. Hopefully, by the time he learns to drive, he will do up his seat belt. All the other children do, but it was constant threats and vocal control that did it, and I do not have that with Reid in the car, because the auditory environment is screaming out of control. Using an FM in the car would overcome this problem.

Even if you usually use a car to go places, the child should be taken to ride on a subway, a bus, or a train. The acoustical considerations of the car and traffic are worse on public transit. Speech is impossible. On the Toronto subway I said, "Sit!" Reid jumped off his seat saying, "This is it." as he moved to the door. If the subway is your usual method of getting around, remember the child cannot see anything but endless backsides, or knees and can hear little of what you say. An FM would be beneficial. The child might find it especially difficult to balance on a bus or train if he is one of the many hard-of-hearing children with balance problems. Public transit systems give the child the ability to go places and do things independently when they are older. The child who is hard of hearing should have as much experience as possible, so that he can have this independence, anywhere in the world.

Figure 13.1 Time to Turn Off the Hearing Aid.

On the ferries between mainland Canada and Vancouver Island, there are signs on every door that say "Passengers wearing hearing aids are warned that the ship's whistle will be sounded during the voyage." Most people just turn their hearing aids off, unless they want to talk. The harmonics of the ship's horn are exquisite, but not to anyone wearing hearing aids.

Unless the theater is set up with a specialized sound system, there may be no point in taking the hard-of-hearing child to the theater. We went to see Victor Borge. The piano music was easy to hear, but I could not hear his dialogue. Somebody behind us must have been hard of hearing, because his wife repeated every line. I listened to her instead of Mr.Borge.

Understanding under what conditions it will always be difficult for a hard-of-hearing child to hear, and creating the best acoustic environment you can, makes their job of learning to listen just a little easier.

Chapter 14
Learning to Live With a Child
Who Wears Hearing Aids:
The Daily Chores
to Promote Good Hearing
. . . and the Frustrations

The similarity between an uncooked egg and a hearing aid in terms of fragility is remarkable, except the egg can get wet. Every time the hearing aids are put in a baby or child's ears, they should be listened to and the Ling Five-Sounds Test (See Chapter 7) performed. This may seem like overkill, but most little children are hard on their hearing aids. One mother had fifty trips to the hearing aid dealer the first year her son had hearing aids. The child was an ordinary two-year-old boy. The hearing aids had trouble keeping up.

The child must learn to clap for each of the sounds in the test. Once the child can reliably clap for each sound, then you do not have to listen to the hearing aids each time they are put back during the day. If it seems the day is spent listening to hearing aids and putting them back in the child's ears and you are convinced you are the only parent who ever had to put up with this . . . you are not. You and the child will become experts with this practice.

The last thing you do for your child at night is the Ling Five-Sounds Test while listening to each hearing aid with a stethoscope. At night you are checking the sound of the hearing aid for clarity and the strength of the batteries for power. A tired battery can rejuvenate overnight enough to pass a quick check, then dies and the hearing aid is non-functioning for the rest of the day. A tired battery means that the hearing aid works with less strength so the sound is weaker, and that is not what the audiologist ordered. Listening to the hearing aid every night ensures consistent quality of sound because your ear will be used to what is normal. You will recognize undesirable trends. If the hearing aid sounds different, take it to the hearing aid dealer.

We use a three-way check on the hearing aid function, every night. First, the Ling Five-Sounds Test using microphone, second, listening to a conversation at maximum earshot, and, thirdly, a quick evaluating of the general background noise. All these things should sound the same every day.

Every night, after the little darling has gone to bed, do not put those hearing aids away until you have listened to them. Check the earmolds for wax or dirt. Disconnect the hearing aids and clean the earmolds with a mild soap and water if they are dirty. I use a crochet hook to reach dirt that just will not come out. My hearing aid dealer recommends not putting things like needles or bobby pins into the earmolds, especially if the earmold is one of the more complicated designs like a **Killian 8 CR** or a **CFA 4.** Sometimes the best advice has to be tempered with reality. You can get a rubber blower at a radio shop to blow the tubing dry. Or you can suck air through the tubes into your mouth until the tubes are dry. Blowing in with your mouth does not work because your breath is humid. Never use a hair dryer.

Once you have a routine for all this, it only takes a half a minute per hearing aid to listen and determine function and power, a minute to wash the earmolds when necessary, a little longer to dry them. Now the hearing aids are ready for the next morning. Turn them off and put them in the **only one place** in the house where ideally they always should be kept.

All the hearing aid manufacturers recommend batteries not be kept in the hearing aids in case they leak. Some hearing aids like our older **Widex** have no On/Off switches. If the battery basket is shut, the hearing aid is on, therefore the battery must be removed. Most hearing aids now have On/Off switches. We make sure the hearing aids are off and leave the batteries in so our mornings do not begin with figuring out which side of the battery is "up."

If you are fumble-fingered and dopey at night, you can do everything but the battery power check in the morning. We prefer to have the hearing aids checked and ready to go the night before, because there is enough to do before the bus at eight o'clock. It is important not to just stick the hearing aids into the child's ears with a short prayer for continued technical brilliance. God has nothing to do with hearing aid maintenance. That is the parent's job.

Many children instantly love their hearing aids. Some children learn to love their hearing aids in a short time, say several weeks. The occasional child will be stubborn and resistant for two years. When Reid was a baby he liked his hearing aids in his mouth better. The joy of hearing was nothing compared to the joy of chewing. I was in earshot, because I was always picking up the hearing aids and taking the earmolds out of his mouth.

Reid's abilities, as a baby, to drop a hearing aid when I was not looking were astounding. Once I crawled the length of a mall, under every counter of every store, looking for a hearing aid. After that, we looked for the hearing aids every ten minutes and every time we changed locations. His hair was cut so that the hearing aids would show. A visual check is better than a touch check because you call attention to the hearing aids every time you touch them. Eventually we want the child to consider them a part of himself. By the time Reid was four, we could go longer without looking at his head to see if the hearing aids were there. I expect I will check for his hearing aids before he goes off to college.

I was privileged to be with a mother and child when a hearing aid disappeared. Reid and John had been in a "Ball Crawl" (a large wading pool full of little plastic balls) so both mothers jumped in and started looking. The management slinked by smirking at us. Sara had sniffed this out as a threatening place and had not wanted John there in the first place, so I felt responsible too, but Reid jumped in, John followed and both children were having a terrific time until John's hearing aid disappeared.

Sara started to act like I do when a hearing aid is missing. She would look for the hearing aid, then check John's ears and pockets, then look for the hearing aid again and despair of finding it. She would get mad at the child, who was totally relaxed about the loss. John would try to help for two seconds and Sara went back to looking. John lost interest. Sara berated herself. I was at the bottom of the ball crawl enjoying the experience and trying to be supportive. Because it was not Reid's hearing aid, I could see the possibilities were finite. After fifteen minutes, Sara found the earmold up near the top. Five minutes later I found the hearing aid at the bottom. We emerged victorious. The manager managed a snide, "Did you enjoy yourselves?" as I took him a sample of junk from the bottom. I relished telling him we were looking for a six-hundred dollar hearing aid the size of his baby finger, but that we had found it.

It was a momentous occurrence because I saw somebody else do what I do when a hearing aid is lost. Losing a hearing aid is a time of extreme stress for the parent, yet we are supposed to be cool and never blame the child. Still, a small voice inside says, "If he really liked the hearing aids, he would not let this happen. He would not take them out. Why doesn't he know when one hearing aid is gone and show me where?"

As two-year-old Reid regularly pitched out the hearing aids, my hysteria became harder to deal with. We developed a game called "losing the hearing aid." I would hide the hearing aid, Reid would have to find it. At first, the hearing aid was put where Reid could see it, then it was left in more remote spots. Reid learned to put the hearing aid in my hand. One day he took it out and put it in my hand. We had a party.

We bought a bag for the hearing aids, cases, batteries, crochet hook, small flashlight and Vitamin E oil. This bag lives on top of the fridge. The hearing aids can be in Reid's ears, in my hand, or in the bag. Nowhere else.

When he was two, Reid threw a hearing aid out the car window. We were on a highway on which it is possible to stop. The hearing aid shrieked as it went out the window. My friend stayed with Reid while I walked back my stopping distance and started searching. The hearing aid was lying on the soft shoulder, still shrieking. Only a plastic cover was missing, which was about ten feet away.

The noise of the road, the wind, the engine masks anything I might want to say to Reid in the car. Even though we wanted him to always wear his hearing aids, there seemed little point in the car. For about a year, we took the hearing aids off before setting out. Getting close to five years old, Reid wore his hearing aids in the car for short trips, but usually decided to take them out after twenty minutes, and gave them to the driver who put them in the change drawer.

Tornados have done less damage to my house than I have done looking for a lost hearing aid, and tornados cost us nineteen trees and a car in 1989. Reid has, over the years, put his hearing aids in the dish pan, the dog bowl, the dog food, the fire place, the sand pile, under his bed, the doll house, the laundry basket, down the heat ducts, in the garbage, and one dropped down the inside of the wall from the upstairs. We had to rip out a foot of newly painted and plastered wall in the dining room to get the hearing aid which was singing a faint song in the wall. Ross used the other hearing aid and the stethoscope to pinpoint which section of wall had to be removed.

Sometimes Reid is trying to punish me, sometimes it just happens. I try not to retaliate when the disappearance happens on purpose, but I focus his attention on the lost hearing aid. If he resorts to being deaf, I resort to sign, "Where hearing aid?" While I am rushing around madly churning things out, which can last twenty-four hours, he is not allowed to have any fun. Rewards are offered to the rest of the family, which get bigger as time passes and the search seems more hopeless.

When the hearing aid is found, Reid is taken to the immediate vicinity and asked to find the hearing aid. Faced by a more calm, but exhausted mother, he finds it easily. The ultimate responsibility for the hearing aids must always end with Reid. This seemed like a tough call when he was two or three, but by the time he was four, he had learned that life became unpleasant with a lost hearing aid. He stopped losing them, or at least using them as weapons. At about four-and-a-half, he stopped taking them out, except to go to bed or to go swimming and I started gaining weight from lack of exercise.

The other factor which reduced the stress of losing the hearing aids was to get them insured. Most insurance companies will not consider hearing aids insurable, even on a rider on your household insurance. Our insurance agent went to eleven companies before he found one which would insure the hearing aids. At a cost of eighty dollars a year, the hearing aids are insured at replacement cost. This is highway robbery, but worth every penny because it takes the edge off my despair when a hearing aid disappears.

Hearing aids are a nuisance in the spring when it rains and in the summer when it is hot and the tubes fill up with little drops of water or sweat. Hearing aids are not so bad in the fall when it is warm and the sun shines, but when it rains they are back to being a nuisance again. Hearing aids are the biggest nuisance in the fifteen months of cold winter we have in Canada. Without a hat the ears get cold, the batteries get cold and weak. With a hat the hearing aids feedback so they are removed or turned off. Hearing aids function best inside a building. Outside, the weather and the world conspire to reduce the instrument's usefulness.

A child happily digging in a sand pile is probably burying the hearing aids. The grains of sand stick to the earmolds, get inside the battery casing and over the contact points, in the microphone, and speaker. The little blower from the radio store does a good job at blowing the sand away, but sand in a hearing aid causes interesting distortion, requiring a trip to the hearing aid dealer for serious cleaning. Reid wears his hearing aids in the sandpile. While the odds favor damage, there is a chance nothing will happen.

Water in a wading pool is another enemy of the hearing aid. A wading pool is no fun unless you get yourself and everyone around you completely wet. Reid does not wear his hearing aids in the wading pool or the bath tub, for the chance is 100 percent that he will get them as wet as the water. When he has finished with the wading pool and his hair is semi-dry, the hearing aids are put back on. Other parents have used plastic food wrap to waterproof the hearing aids so that they can be used in a wading pool. New on the market are hearing aid waterproof covers in wild colors which look like little uninflated balloons.

A hearing aid dryer is a plastic bag or jar with a renewable can of silica inside. Do not put the batteries or earmolds into the dryer. Take the batteries out, take the hooks off the casings and put the hearing aids into the hearing aid dryer until they are dry. Be sure to test the hearing aids with the Ling Five-Sounds Test at close range, at maximum earshot and listen to background noise for distortion. A hearing aid could sound fine initially, but could be corroding inside. The distortion could become obvious days later. Remember that the hearing aids were wet, and keep listening critically.

Feedback is caused by sound escaping around the earmold and back into the microphone of the hearing aid. It is the same as when someone puts a microphone too close to a speaker at a school concert. While feedback is occurring, all sound going into the hearing aid is obliterated. The solution is usually new earmolds. Sometimes, hearing aids will feedback if there is wax in the ear canal. Cleaning out the wax will solve the problem. Sometimes the hearing aids feed back when the child has a middle ear infection. See your physician if you suspect a middle ear infection. Infrequently, the cause of feedback is a broken casing on the hearing aid. This is the problem if the feedback continues even when you put your finger over the receiver or ear hook to block it.

The most common cause of feedback in growing children is outgrown earmolds. If you have to buy new shoes for bigger feet, you will probably have to buy new earmolds. I used to think that I spent a lot of money on Reid's shoes when he was two, but it was not the shoes, it was the price of shoes and hearing aid earmolds together that destroyed the family budget. From babyhood to three years, it is not uncommon to have to replace the earmolds every six weeks. After Reid's third birthday, earmold replacement slowed down to every three months, and after his fourth birthday, we got six to eight months out of an earmold.

The greater the hearing loss, the greater the gain required and the sooner the earmolds begin to feedback. Turning the volume down on the hearing aid is a temporary fix because the child will not hear as well. The only solution is new earmolds immediately. There is a terrible time to survive between ordering new earmolds and getting them. Feedback will drive your friends away, the family will not come visiting. Even the teacher of the deaf will say, "Can't you do anything about that noise?" When you point out that new earmolds are coming, the teacher will usually suggest that it would be nice if they arrived before class.

It is unfair to blame the child for feedback. Any sane parent recognizes that. As the days go by waiting for new earmolds, the child gets into trouble because the parents' normal tolerance for childish behavior has been annihilated by the constant squealing. The solution is simple. Tell the hearing aid dealer that the noise is unbearable. Have the impressions sent out by rush service to the earmold makers. Impressions received at the mold makers by 7 A.M. are made into earmolds by 5 P.M. The mold makers are not usually set up for consumers and prefer to deal with the hearing aid dealers. This business liaison is well planned, but involves periods of waiting at several stages. When that period of waiting is causing a parent to get angry at a child, by-pass the formal waiting time. Ten days turn-around on earmolds is unnecessary, it can be done in twenty-four hours at slightly higher cost.

While you are at the hearing aid dealer's, he can build up the leaking earmold with a coat or two of liquid mold material, which is sold to the dealers as **Acouseal.** It goes on like nail polish, dries quickly and stops the feedback temporarily. A tiny bottle is thirty-five dollars, but they will not sell it to parents.

As you learn to live with hearing aids so does the child. After a couple of years, you will have encountered every panic situation imaginable and will start to be quite good at dealing with a crisis. About the same time, the child will also learn to live with his hearing aids. All that experience you have built up will never need to be used again. Feedback is a problem that goes on forever, until the child grows up and leaves home to take a spouse, and the spouse will take over your job of telling the child to push his hearing aid in because it is squealing.

Chapter 15
Not Deaf Enough

A person who has hearing problems does not want to begin a business or social encounter with, "Hi. I'm a 50 percent hearing impaired, auditorily challenged, deaf-as-a-door knob, hearing aid user." He will say, "I'm John."

Audiologists rank hearing loss by decibels and Hertz. Educators label the children as having a hearing loss which is mild, moderate, severe, profound, or total. Members of the Deaf community evaluate other people with hearing problems by how much hearing is available and rapidly convert from "Deaf like me," to "hard of hearing," not like me, especially if speech is obvious. We use labels in casual conversation, then other people come along and formalize those labels within a professional or societal setting. An educational audiologist, Riza Razack has identified fourteen different sets of labels for hard-of-hearing children, from medical, educational, societal, and Deaf community sources. The same word can have quite different meanings, depending on who is using it.

You may meet a person with a severe loss who speaks well, who calls himself "hard of hearing." He may feel no kinship with the Deaf community. He considers himself not impaired and uses "hard of hearing", because it is the simplest way to describe his situation. The preschool teachers said Reid was "hard of hearing." I felt the term did not adequately cover his problems. My grandfather was "deaf." He spoke classical Greek, Latin, and English. I had a friend who was "deaf-mute." Most of her family could not hear or speak. We spent hours together, doing things, looking at things, and miming. In my family of doctors, the term "deaf-mute" was only used after speech was not evident, otherwise a person with hearing problems was "deaf." When the preschool teacher labeled Reid "hard of hearing" I had trouble with the term because it clashed with my own vocabulary.

For many parents, the word "deaf" has bad connotations probably because our parents or grandparents typically used the terms "deaf and dumb," a false and misleading stereotype. The Scribner Dictionary defines"deaf" as: (adjective) **1.** unable to hear **2.** unwilling to hear or pay regard. It says nothing about speech. "Deaf-and-dumb" is a separate entry:(adjective) unable to hear or speak. "Deaf-mute" means one who is congenitally deaf and has not learned to speak. There are no entries for hearing-impaired. My friend, Marleen told me she did not feel so bad about her child's mild/moderate hearing impairment, but she could not stand it if he were deaf. It all comes down to the word which we hear most often and with which we feel comfortable.

If the people around us are stuck on labelling a child by degree of hearing loss, perhaps it is because they are trying to provide services for a child based on what was done for other children with similar losses. A problem comes when the parents' experience clashes with the labels. In ordinary daily life, you will hear "deaf" used to describe your child who wears hearing aids by anyone other than those in the medical or educational professions. People do not do this to be mean, they are being natural within their own vocabulary. Don't try to correct someone else's vocabulary. Listen to them. Every person who commented that Reid wore hearing aids or was deaf, gave me a particle of information which helped down the road. Usually people who noticed, were people who had relatives with hearing aids. Hearing aids are not noticed by people unless they have learned to look for them.

There will always be children who have better hearing and children who have less hearing than your child. There is no elitism associated with extremes of hearing loss. You can't be jealous of the child with more hearing and denigrate his parent's frantic attempts to deal with the child's loss by saying, "Well, your child is not **deaf** like mine." Parents of children with hearing problems must pull together and learn from each other, rather than accept segregation by a label of function. To be isolated by a label of loss, or category of hearing loss either self-adopted, or given by other parents or professionals, is wrong.

When Reid was three, I felt that the isolation from other parents facing the same problems as I, was detracting from my ability to be a good parent. I wrote an open letter describing myself and gave it to the preschool teacher. She gave the note to a mother who invited Reid and me for lunch.

We sat at her kitchen table for six hours and talked. We had so much in common, the same services, the same technology, the same teacher, whom we assessed as a ray of sunshine in our sometimes gloomy lives. She said she had been hesitant to meet, because she had met other parents who spent the whole time telling her that it was worse to have a child with a profound hearing loss. It seemed to her that the only parents around all had children with profound losses and they all believed that the problems of the hard-of-hearing child with a mild or moderate hearing loss were not very important.

This attitude carries through to the government and the educational bureaucracy and sometimes to the professionals who help with your child. I think it goes back to their schooling. The academics teach by examples of extremes, because the differences are more easily discerned by the students. Unfortunately, the students take home the idea that only the extremes are important. As one audiologist said to another, gleefully, "I found a fascinating case today, no response to the audiometer." To the audiologist, a flat response is rare. They have to be allowed their moments of professional interest in strange and unique cases.

I think a great audiologist diagnoses the lesser losses which are creating havoc for children. She has to be good to be able to test children who are down ten or twenty decibels and so used to hearing and coping like this, that they can ignore the hearing that is missing, cruising right through childhood until the teacher insists on terminal endings in writing, or past tenses.

At age four, Reid was missing real clarity in his production of the higher sounds such as **ch k f th ss sh**. He had a little thuddy sound which he used indiscriminately. The speech pathologist suggested it was developmental, meaning he would grow into producing those sounds clearly when he was ready, she also suggested that this deficiency seemed slight to her and of no great concern. The speech pathologist is the objective assessor of Reid's language, I am the subjective assessor on a daily basis. The deficiency seemed more than slight to me. We focused work on those sounds rather than waiting for natural development.

If I had sat back and done nothing for Reid, following the recommendations for children with mild and moderate losses, he would not yet be talking and achieving literacy would have been doubtful. If he had been born one hundred years ago, he might have ended up the village idiot, who understood some speech, was not stone deaf, but who never amounted to much and was a drag on the general economy. Yet there are all these people who continue to say, "Relax, it will all turn out fine."

Cassy was another child with a mild hearing problem in our school. She was older than Reid. I networked to meet her mother and have coffee. She declined. Perhaps she is too busy, or perhaps she does not think of her child as "hard of hearing." Maybe the last thing she wants to do is meet another parent with a hard-of-hearing child, especially one who is turning the community upside down to ensure equal opportunities. Sometimes I wondered if the other mother, who seemed very laid back about the whole thing, might not have a better key to survival than I do.

Gossip came home regularly from school. My children were amazed because Cassy did not always wear her hearing aids and went to school without any of the technological devices which we have utilized for Reid. When we hit the school system and requested FMs and teacher training, there was already a certain expectation of "what will be done for children wearing hearing aids in our school" based on previous experience with other children. Believe me, Reid always wears his hearing aids and his teacher uses the FM and does not shout at him from across a room!

Hard-of-hearing children going into the school system often have a three-year lag in language attainment on arrival. This looks pretty bad, but actually the child is only a year behind his hearing age, which is how long the aids have been used regularly. His chronological age is five, his hearing age is three, his speech age is two.

Achievements and expectations for most children with hearing problems are abysmally low. The majority of profoundly deaf children achieve grade three-to six reading levels as adults. No matter how high your aspirations are for your child, if he reads at a grade three-to-six level, he does not have many choices in a literate society. It is inappropriate to extrapolate from studies of profoundly deaf children to children with mild losses. Probably a child with a mild hearing loss is going to have a higher reading level than a child with a profound loss, but there was little study made of children with mild hearing losses. Children with mild losses often fail grade three. It is often the failure in school which results in a diagnosis of hearing problems in the first place. Before that, they coast on their exceptionally well-developed coping skills.

I have a slight mild hearing loss. I function with the same loss as Reid has in his good ear when it is working well. My nights are passages of blackness. All the sounds which annoy Ross and keep him awake are silent to me. I cannot hear the telephone ring, but can turn the dial to 2 and hear even the quietest of my friends speak. I cannot hear conversations across a living room. I am losing my sense of humor because at least half of every good joke is missing. I never tell secrets because I cannot hear them when people lower their voices to tell me something confidential.

The fact that I have a mild hearing loss has given me a significant advantage in understanding the seriousness of Reid's loss in every aspect of his life.

The last two times I have been in formal educational settings, at a conference and a seminar, I actually wished that I had an FM because it was so hard for me to hear. By the time the speaker finished with a concept and discussion, I was still working on sorting it all out. Then I would have to pick up the next concept halfway through and muddle around. When people in an audience have questions to ask, I cannot hear them at all and have to guess what the question was from the answer.

Ross speaks clearly to Reid and mumbles around a pipe to me, then berates me for asking what he said. He talks in a low voice and lowers it more when he wants to make a point (an old advertising trick). Then he waits three days and tells me something more, when I did not hear him at all the first time and was not aware of his information. He gets annoyed when I keep asking him the same question, but if it is something important like, "Did you put enough money in the bank to cover the oil check?" it is not good enough to hope he did. My children all talk to their feet. When they whine, I do not tell them to speak up. That is convenient.

In a noisy environment, I move closer to the speaker, who keeps moving away. I have learned people repeat things once and cannot comprehend that their message was not as clear as a bell the second time around. I laugh when others do, even though I do not know why. When I insist that a speaker address me clearly, or rephrase a message, the scorn "You can't hear me? I can't believe you cannot hear me." makes me wince.

I experience every day what a child with a mild hearing loss has to deal with. I have the advantage of already being literate and lingual. I do not speechread as well as Reid who is a natural born speechreader. Partial messages from friends, family, teachers, siblings all get a little confused. People say the television is loud, I only notice when it is distorted.

It is no surprise that children who hear the way I do, fail. It is amazing that they can get along for so long and so well, all things considered.

> A child with a mild/moderate hearing loss, or a child who is wearing a hearing aid which is not coupled to an FM unit in the classroom, may appear to hear just fine. However, in reality, the child may hear the teacher's voice and the intonation patterns, but may not hear individual speech sounds clearly enough to differentiate one word from another, **(Bess, [1985]; Dobie & Berlin, [1979])**. Words like "ladder," "leader," and "little," may all sound the same to a child with poor intelligibility. Words like "talked," "talks," and "talking," may all sound like "alk". Yet, if the teacher were to ask the child, "Do you hear me?" the child would likely respond, "Yes." One would not expect a young child to answer, "I hear your voice, but I can't hear the unstressed linguistic markers of plurality and tense; nor can I hear articles, voiceless consonants, or new vocabulary words clearly enough to distinguish from other known words." Yet, educators are surprised when this same child evidences a lack of vocabulary, a poor intuitive feel for linguistic structure, and trouble keeping up with the "slow" reading group.
> **Flexer et al. (1989)**

It is even more amazing that these children with minimal hearing losses have any egos left. They have to survive on their own, in spite of the professionals, and other hard-of-hearing people who say that they do not really have a problem. They do not even have the label of "hearing problems" to help them. They get evaluated for being noisy, for behaving badly, not paying attention, not trying hard enough, and not listening. The actual cause of the behaviors is often ignored. They are not deaf enough for any further concern.

It was estimated by Dr. Frederick S. Berg in 1986 that of thirty-nine-and-a half million school children in the United States, about eight million children have some degree of hearing loss. This same study found only 1 percent of the hard-of-hearing children in schools are getting the help they need to be in mainstreamed classrooms.

Chapter 16
A Parent's Consideration
of Sign Language
and Speechreading

Sign Languages

Many people who refer to themselves as "**Deaf**," with a capital **D**, say they belong to a separate culture, made distinct by the use of sign language instead of speech. Being **Deaf** displays a difference similar to being from another country, or having another nationality, language and culture.

Perhaps in the United States, the "Deaf "culture is stronger simply by virtue of numbers. In Canada, there are partial "Deaf" communities in which Deaf people work and play, but they are not born and educated in those communities. The hearing world surrounds the "Deaf" culture and for the most part ignores its existence. There is some recognition of the culture when the two must meet, but while the **Deaf** person is proud of sign language, the hearing person more often sees it as compensation for the disability of deafness.

When Reid was first diagnosed, I expected the Deaf mother of one of my friends to help me give the child a great start by sharing mother lore. Well, despite her son's suggestions, she signed, "Oh, he's hard of hearing. We don't have anything in common." At the time we knew little about hearing loss and were focused on the word "deaf." Perhaps she was wise, but I felt a door slammed in my face, which has continued throughout Reid's childhood, just about every time I have encountered members of the **Deaf** culture.

Given the technology-limited status of hearing aids, and the lack of access to realistic therapy, preschool and parent/infant programs in the 1950's and 1960's, it is not surprising that many people in the Deaf community feel that auditory/oral education did not serve them well. There are many other people for whom the choice was appropriate. If we look back to that period, it is amazing that anybody learned to talk, considering the limitations of auditory trainers then. The technological developments of the 1970's and 1980's have pushed the line of "deafness" further back. Academic and practical developments in teaching speech and language to hard-of-hearing children have blossomed.

Since second language learning is required in Ontario, I wondered if Reid might like to learn a sign language instead of French. I ended up going to a workshop on American Sign Language (ASL) at the school for the Deaf. In the afternoon the workshop became a consciousness-raising session for the hearing parents with deaf children. The hostility of some full-fledged members of the Deaf community towards "hard-of-hearing" people, meaning anyone who spoke relatively normally and had a less-than-profound loss, reverberated around the room. Parents like me who had come prepared to learn about ASL were not prepared to be targets for the anger that discussion groups fomented. In the car driving home, I kept telling myself that it was wise not to stand up and try to share the difficulties of parenting my child who might want choices himself in the future, which I did not want closed off for him. It just was not the time.

On the other hand, when **is** the time? These Deaf people are blaming the auditory/oral education of today for the failures of the past when hearing aids and amplification devices were barely out of the Model-T stage; there were no public school preschools or parent/infant programs. The schools were not even required to try and provide an education for children with disabilities. The improvements in quality of hearing aids and other amplifiers in just the past few years have brought them from the level of a Model-T Ford to a Rolls-Royce.

Stories about oralism have been embellished and become legends. I would not beat Reid if he signed. He does get transported to his bedroom if he refuses to wear his aids and left there until he changes his mind. If he chooses to remember me as an oralist tyrant when he grows up, I will be sad, because I am only trying to help him.

The teachers of one hundred years ago, of twenty years ago and of the present were and are trying to help the children. Most teachers develop allegiances to signing or oral methods (oral, auditory-oral, auditory-verbal, Cued Speech) early in their careers and become more convinced as to the merits of their choice and the failings of the opposite camp. Their knowledge of what they are condemning is limited by their training and experience as they move further into their own choice. Meanwhile, parents of children who are experiencing difficulties with various methods (sign or oral) find it confusing. So much of what they hear about the other side is biased. I think most parents want a happy child who grows up into a happy adult. The continued bickering can result in unhappy parents and an unhappy child.

Peace might come in the next generation. The **Deaf** are fighting for recognition as a group of people. Past generations of hearing people have been mean to deaf people, not even allowing them to own property, according to Oliver Sacks in *Seeing Voices* (1989). Concessions have to be made on both sides, the **Deaf** have to recognize they are the statistically small part of a huge group of people who have difficulty hearing. A child with a mild hearing loss is probably not going to learn to sign and is probably not going to move into the **Deaf** culture because he is more hearing than deaf. But if Reid decides **he** would rather learn ASL than French, I would support his decision.

Another teaching method, total communication, involves the parent speaking and signing at the same time, producing English sentences with correct word order. There are various systems of signed English, one of them is called Signing Exact English. Total communication was developed as a compromise between speech and sign, but like all compromises has its drawbacks. The **Deaf** in the **Deaf** community use ASL habitually, and do not sign with Signing Exact English, while the hearing need the correct order of English words in order to understand them.

Many **Deaf** people are actively promoting ASL as a standard language throughout the United States and Canada. ASL is a full language. Like most people, my first reaction to hearing about ASL was, "Wow, an Esperanto. I could learn this and travel the world," but it is not international. ASL is the native language of some **Deaf** children of **Deaf** parents. **Deaf** parents comprise about 5 percent of the total group of parents who have deaf or hard-of-hearing children.

The only time that Reid has been exposed to sign has been at the school for the Deaf. This was a total communication institution in which the teachers signed and spoke and the students were supposed to sign and speak and did so in class, but the emphasis is on signing. Out of class, the students signed amongst themselves and usually did not speak. This school was a very quiet school even though the students were speaking volumes as they walk from class to class. What you heard was laughter. In response to the request of the **Deaf** community, this school is now primarily an ASL school with a "Bi-program" available for those who wish total communication.

At a meeting at the school for the **Deaf** there were hearing and deaf parents, teachers, students, and members of the **Deaf** community. Every possible mode of communication was used. When a presentation was manual,(signed) an interpreter translated the manual language to English. The interpreter's voice was not as loud as the other voices coming through the main microphone had been, not loud enough to be heard by people who depend on hearing aids. A lady got up and signed her presentation. Four-year-old Reid could not hear the interpreter and asked me, "Mummy, where's her voice?" I told him, "She is talking with her hands." Reid watched, fascinated that this was talking. He had never seen more than one or two gestures at a time, usually dealing with what he wanted to eat. Then he turned to me and said, "I can talk with my hands too, see I can say, 'Get lost.' "

To see a child develop signing abilities is dramatic. Little fingers fly and the child can express his desires and ideas much sooner than the auditory-verbal child. Signing is dramatic and catches the interest of the hearing world, even though the message is not understood. Once a hard-of-hearing child learns to talk, he ceases to be remarkable. He is just another child who happens to wear hearing aids. We should never lose our awareness of the drama of speech and the freedom it gives our children.

Aside from languages like ASL or invented forms like Signing Exact English which use gesture and position of the hands to represent words, actions, or ideas, there are also methods which use gesture to replace voice in a language. Fingerspelling is used within the signed languages to spell out words for which there are no signs. It is not difficult to learn the twenty six letters and ten numbers. The receiver must decode each letter, process it back into a word and place the word in a sentence while watching the next letter. I.F. Y.O.U. S.P.E.L.L. O.U.T. A. S.E.N.T.E.N.C.E. L.E.T.T.E.R. B.Y. L.E.T.T.E.R. it takes time and effort. Most people read and write faster than they fingerspell.

Cued Speech was developed by Orin Cornett in 1966 when he discovered the difficulty of speechreading spoken English. Cued Speech uses gesture to partially replace the speech sounds of language. Eight handshapes represent groups of consonant sounds, and four positions about the face represent groups of vowel sounds. Combinations of the handshapes and placements show the exact pronunciation of words as they are spoken and cued. Cued speech can be learned in a matter of hours. Those who use the method are enthusiastic. (See Sue Schwartz, *Choices in Deafness*, [1987] for further information.)

Speechreading

Why can some people speechread so well? According to the laws of physics and physiology, the bumblebee cannot fly. His wingspan is too small for his body weight. Nobody told the bumble bee, he gets up every morning and he flies. When we talk to our babies, we look at them, they look at us. They hear sounds, but also see our lips move and feel airstream on their faces. Babies put it all together and eventually can understand speech without seeing faces.

During the early development of the auditory-verbal method, many parents "trying to do their best for the child" carried out the child's therapy at home, around the clock. David Colley in *Sound Waves* (1985) relates that "Mardie was not allowed to lipread, a natural instinct of all deaf children." Following one of the basic principles of Helen Beebe, the parents covered their mouths every time they spoke to a hard-of-hearing child. (Ling, *Early Intervention for Hearing-Impaired Children; Oral Options*, 1984). No one would think of doing this to a hearing child. I cover my mouth only to do the Ling Five-Sounds Test. It is the hearing aids' function I am interested in, not Reid's abilities to speechread **ah ee ou sh ss**. Reid lets us know how he feels about a hand over a mouth by putting his hands over his ears.

According to Dr. Ling in *Foundations of Spoken Language for Hearing-Impaired Children* (1989), proponents of the auditory-verbal philosophy recommend spending **part of each lesson** developing auditory skills through the deliberate suppression of speechreading skills. Speechreading is necessary for most hard-of-hearing children under many real-life conditions, but "maximum use of residual hearing and maximum auditory/visual performance can result only when such focus is given to audition." (Ling, 1989, p127). Judith Simser recalls, "When I first went to Dr. Agnes Ling Phillips and Dr. Daniel Ling in Montreal in 1966, my son, Scott was taught mainly through hearing. Rather than covering my mouth, I sat beside him or he sat on my lap while we played. Scott could lipread well and would do it under poor acoustic conditions, when conversing with friends and on many daily occasions in the home."

When Reid was a baby, our first encounter was with a teacher who used the Beebe unisensory approach. Her insistence on not using the child's natural speechreading abilities to make sense of spoken language resulted in our dismissal of the auditory-verbal approach at that time. Practically everyone uses speechreading to some extent. It is tough enough to live with a hard-of-hearing child without taking away a natural aid to language.

I never did anything to teach Reid to speechread beyond positioning myself so he could see me talk, most of the time. We know it is a major part of his ability to communicate. My niece and I took our two four-year-old boys to a restaurant with a playroom. When it was time to leave, I caught Reid's eye through the window and said, "One more slide, then put on your socks and shoes, and come up here." Reid went down the slide, put on his socks and shoes and came to me. My niece had to go and shout at Eric to do the same thing. Eric's speech is better than Reid's, but his speechreading skills are not as good. I am told Reid is lucky to have these skills naturally. Other children must work hard to learn to speechread.

I believe that speechreading helps and does not hinder speech. Reid is given every opportunity to speechread, without making any issue over the fact that he does it naturally.

Chapter 17
Day Care, Babysitters and the Outside World: Making Sure Other People Help Your Child When You Are Not There

Before Reid arrived in our lives, we knew little about hearing problems, especially in children. My "Auntie" Kay grew progressively "deafer" all her life. She had a hearing aid, which never seemed to work very well. My Mother would caution me, "Now, Auntie Kay does not hear well, so you have to speak slowly and shout at her." She did some speechreading, but we were doing everything wrong and made it more difficult for her. We shouted, we kept repeating the same words, we sat on opposite sides of the living room. We often gave up and pretended that we really had not said anything all that important. If only I had learned to sit close to her and to expand confused messages. Auntie Kay sometimes would lead us to use varied vocabulary, or to expand a message by processing out loud what she thought she had heard, but conversations often ended up with a sense of "riddle-me-ree" and exhaustion, probably on both sides.

A hearing problem is such a common thing that we should have learned better methods of communicating with hard-of-hearing people as a matter of social graces. We have not. When a child is diagnosed, we learn things which will make life easier for the child and can apply that specific learning outwards to other people with hearing problems. Life becomes just a little easier.

Unitron puts out a pamphlet called *Coping with Hearing Loss: Suggestions for Friends and Family*. These words should be framed and hung on the wall in every living room in the land:

- The support and understanding of family and friends is very important to the hard-of-hearing person. The following simple rules of communication can make conversation easier and more enjoyable for everyone.
- Be sure you have the person's attention, before you begin to speak. It is difficult to hear or lipread if attention is focused elsewhere.
- Look directly at the person while you are speaking. Eye contact is very important. Make sure your face can be seen clearly. Avoid distracting movements such as smoking, chewing or putting your hands in front of your face. Even slightly turning your head can make it much more difficult for the listener to see your eyes or mouth.
- Speak in a normal tone of voice. Do not speak too quickly or exaggerate your lip movements. There is no need to shout. Use appropriate facial expressions, gestures and body language to make it easier for them to understand what you are saying.
- Reword your sentence if the person does not understand. Do not repeat the same word over and over. Some words are easier to hear or lipread than others. Try to use other words which have the same meaning.
- Be aware of competing noises or sounds in the room. Music, air conditioners and other people talking in the same room can be very disturbing. To improve listening, move away from the noise so your voice can be more easily heard by the person with the hearing problem.
- Ask if there is anything you can do to improve the listening situation. You can reduce the difficulty and frustration experienced by many hard-of-hearing people by asking for their suggestions.

Unitron, *Coping with Hearing Loss: Suggestions for Friends and Family*, Canada E86.02 530-029-000.

Knowing how much easier it is to hear when the speaker is within earshot, I want to teach the world to move in closer so my child can hear you, so I can hear you. Anyone who takes responsibility for the child, even for a short period of time must learn the importance of critical distance in communication.

I inundated babysitters with too much information. Between Reid's proclivity for screaming and the barrage of the latest tips I had learned, we went through every teenager within ten miles. It is better to develop a relationship with one or two trusted sitters, preferably with interested mothers in the background, rather than just anyone who will come. The average teenager might not be able to deal with the variations of behavior which a young, hard-of-hearing child can present. I found it more relaxing to go out knowing the child will be happy with a familiar face.

In other situations such as the library story hour, I explained what Reid can hear, rather than what he cannot hear and emphasized not shouting at him. Reid generally moved to the front and coped with the group himself.

Day camp was Reid's first "mainstream" experience. The staff knew nothing about hard-of-hearing children and there were no special considerations. It was good for the rest of his family to see Reid being treated like any other child. It worked out well for a short term placement of fourteen days, but would have been a disaster if it had been a long term. He was exhausted from coping. The child must do more than survive by following the crowd. It made it harder to convince people that there were special considerations which needed to be made for him because he coped so well. Mainstreaming may be desirable, whether day camp or school, but it requires adequate supports to ensure a benefit to the child.

We believe in the Jesuit philosophy of 'give me a child to the age of seven and he is mine for life'. There was never consideration of anybody else bringing up our children. They would not have been born if we hadn't wanted to raise them (with or without physical problems). We were encouraged to consider sending the child to a nursery school by many of the social workers and other professionals we encountered. For several months, Reid attended a part-time day care for handicapped children when he was two. The people in the nursery were wonderful, but Reid was the only child who was going to progress quickly. Consequently he got a lot of attention while he was there. The facilities were fabulous, right down to half-size and quarter-size toilets, large playrooms, terrific acoustics, and a school bus which picked up the children every morning. However, it was not an appropriate placement for him because there was no peer group of children with whom he could learn.

The nearest nursery for deaf children was thirty miles away, too much valuable life time spent on a bus doing nothing, and he would have been in a total communication environment which he did not need because he was starting to speak. I felt strongly that our other children had turned out well without going to day care, and that Reid would benefit from my abilitites to teach him too. We sold our house in the city and bought a house for what was left after the lawyers and real estate agents had their grab. We have since gone into debt up to our eye balls, but that debt will never equal the cost of supporting a hard-of-hearing and possibly unemployable, illiterate adult. With this specter in mind, perhaps it is worth considering: "How much house do you really need?" and "What have all those tax dollars done for you lately?"

Sandra tells her four-year-old boy that "life is a team sport", and he is part of the team, as he goes to preschool and she goes to work. She has none of the personal drive to habituate her child to listening that I do, feeling that the school will take care of the child's problems. Sandra feels her family should not be punished financially by having to live on only one salary instead of two, just because they have a hard-of-hearing child.

The great irony is that **most** parents cannot afford children after pregnancy, and **few** can pay for great day care. With day care training and positions relegated way below the education profession, the outlook is particularly gloomy for children with handicaps. Supporting the family by both parents working part-time and splitting the responsibilities of the child's hearing, speech, and language development, would be an option.

The reality is both parents go to work and park the child at the sitter or day care. The day passes. The parents return home and pick up the child. The child of working parents often sleeps longer during the day and stays up later at night. The working parent is less likely to spend those hours laying down the law, because they have so little time together. The child can be difficult to handle. The parent is preoccupied in getting dinner cooked and cleaned up while shoving laundry from the washer to the dryer. Parents and child are perpetually tired during the one-on-one language, listening and speech-encouragement time. What else can you do?

Any household help, if affordable can give extra hours of language time because some of the chores are done. I know people who romanticize about the companionship of the family cleaning up after supper, all together. These are the same people who think childbirth has something to do with flowers and soft winds. A dishwasher gives a family an extra hour-and-a-half a day to talk to the hard-of-hearing child.

Utilize the resources in your family. Some grandparents are happy to have finished with their own little children. Other grandparents, or aunts and uncles are delighted to be asked to undertake greater responsibilities for a child. If you live reasonably close, perhaps the grandparents would be willing to go to or take the child at some point during the day.

Sometimes, grandparents arrive to clean up the house and do minor repairs for their offspring who failed Home Economics or Shop. While this is wonderful, a grandparent must be careful not to criticize the chaos. The parent is doing as much as she or he can working with the hard-of-hearing child, and possibly holding down a full-time job too, and he or she does not have the strength to do more. The last thing anyone has any right to do is make snide comments like, "How can you stand to live like this?" Barbara Bush said in *Ladies Home Journal*, "But I say to my own daughter, So the house is dirty? The darn trouble with cleaning a house is it gets dirty the next day anyway, so skip it a week if you have to. Children are the most important thing."

A nanny, interested enough to learn all the things you know would be ideal. Royalty commands years of loyalty from the nannies; other parents seem to have new ones all the time. Nannies are a solution for those of the top 1 percent of incomes. If you cannot afford a nanny, next best would be spending the day in a home-care unit with a babysitter who talks too much and never watches soaps. The child needs constant communication with another human being. The right person will inspire the use of speech. Two types of people look after children: those who talk and those who do not talk. Visit a potential sitter and watch the other children's attempts at speech. If the children come up to speak, are listened to and answered reasonably, you have found a sitter. If the other children do not make much attempt to speak, they have probably learned not to speak and you should move on.

Last on my list is the day care center. Financial crushes reduce the quality of care, even if it is a day care center for children with hearing problems. A child with a mild hearing loss stands to get lost in a center for children with hearing problems because of the traditional assumption that these children have no problems beyond needing hearing aids. I do not believe that the preschool years are an appropriate time for sending the child to a place during the day where little is known about his problems. It is easy for the child to be forgotten unless he becomes a monster. The aggressive or assertive children are the ones who get the rewards of attention. Some hard-of-hearing children have a great tendency to go off into a corner and their own world. Others benefit from the exposure to other children, particluarly hearing children. However, it may be the only option available, in which case the parents simply have to make do.

At some point you will have an opportunity to talk to the people involved with your child. This is the best time to share information about making life easier for themselves and the child. If the child has an FM aid, someone will have to teach the caretakers about its use. The FM aid should be checked regularly to make sure it is working. Drop in to the day care center when you are not expected, to see how things are really going. Is the FM on the child or is it sitting in a corner? Is the child happily being part of the group or withdrawing? If things are going well, then that is fine. If not, start looking for another day care center. The child has no time to lose. Every day that passes with inadequate language affects his future.

In the beginning, our friends would tell us about other methods, notably signing. To avoid confrontation we would say, "Thank you," and continue teaching Reid to listen, speak, and speechread. Eventually they learned that Reid was not going to sign and stopped suggesting it. Now, those same friends wisely say, "Ah, I always knew he could really hear." There have been other friends who had suggestions and made them, but stayed to watch what we were doing. As Reid progressed, their suggestions became less frequent, partly because we had evidence of success and partly because they learned that we knew more than they did.

For many parents the choice of a method can be difficult and complex. When Reid was two, and communicating by screeching and throwing himself on the ground, the choice of signing or oral communication was not then as clear to us as it was to the people who were advising us. However, we provided him with a choice. I learned a few gestures, and spoke to him at the same time, always within earshot, and so he could see my face. When he was ready, he chose to speak.

A former roommate who lives in Brazil stopped writing me. I wrote her but there was silence from Sao Paulo. This past summer we got together. She confessed that she had been too frightened to write and ask how Reid was doing, based on her observations as a teacher when Reid was a "terrible two" and speechless. She was stunned that Reid spoke as well as her son who is a chatterbox. I was stunned to learn that Reid had appeared to be in such bad shape to an interested onlooker at age two, but grateful that she kept her gloomy observations to herself until later.

Recently we ran into an audiologist who looked after Reid when he was little. She said "Hello," and Reid started to talk to her. She absolutely beamed and asked, "What method did you use? You have both worked very hard and have accomplished miracles." I said, "We tried them all. We encourage speechreading. The nitty gritty of speech and language is the Ling Method." She said, "Ah." We understood each other. It was uplifting to have someone in the field applaud.

Our friends do not have any concept of how much of our lives we have poured into Reid so that he can succeed. They care, but real understanding is beyond the realm of friendship. We have to understand that there is no reason for them to understand. We have become one of the families with a hard-of-hearing child who speaks. Other people do not really think much about his hearing problems, beyond simple observation that some hard-of-hearing people speak while others sign. At least, some people along the way have learned a little about hearing problems and hearing aids, as our paths have crossed. Perhaps they will carry that knowledge with them to make life easier for someone else in the future.

See **Useful Tips**, p. 206, for information which you can share with your child's day care and babysitters.

Chapter 18
Who Am I? Parent or Teacher?

There's Kanga. She isn't clever, Kanga isn't, but she would be so anxious about Roo that she would do a Good Thing to Do without thinking about it.
A.A.Milne. *Winnie-the-Pooh*, (1926)

Babies arrive with an amazing collection of instinctive skills like sneezing, coughing, startling, (alerting to sights and sounds), rooting, sucking, seeing, and hearing. A newborn's grasp is strong enough to pick him up while he is holding on to a parent's finger. The baby will recoil from pain. Immediately after birth the baby is alert, before slipping into the post-birth sleep that lasts until he goes home to turn night into day. We know babies hear loud external noises *in utero*, because they react to them. They have to be able to hear at birth. They need to build a memory to know what they are hearing.

From the first time a parent smiles at the newborn baby, the job of teaching the child has begun. We begin the biggest job in our human lives with little knowledge. We can do a good job even if we have never seen a baby before. The baby needs warmth, food and protection which the parent instinctively provides. A parent of a handicapped child has a more intense job of caretaking, which will go on for much longer as the child either learns or does not learn to do things for himself. A parent of a hard-of-hearing child has to learn a daunting amount to help the child. The parent must begin to learn while still dealing with the meaning of it all and with rolling waves of anger, grief, fear, and denial.

With the other children in the family, I was never aware of being a teacher. I was their mother, providing full tums and dry bums, and spending the rest of the time doing things with the babies-playing down on their level, looking at books, going for walks, all the things babies and small children do when they are not hungry, wet or tired. I was Reid's mother too and provided the same nurturing for him. Added to Reid's babyhood was a constant worry about his survival and quality of life. Suspecting that he might be hard of hearing meant that every reference to "ears" in the popular "learn to parent" books was scrutinized for more information. There was not much there.

As soon as Reid was diagnosed, an itinerant teacher was sent to us. The process of turning a parent into a teacher began. Nancy Ledger, our first itinerant teacher, brought me lessons every week, from the **Ski-Hi** program on parenting hard-of-hearing children and hearing aid use. Our first lessons involved alerting the six-month baby to every sound. "I heard that? Did you hear that?" while smiling. Nancy has a fabulous face which lights up when she is talking to a baby. Reid would smile and kick and coo while Nancy worked with him. Nancy's visits reassured me Reid was not the only hard-of-hearing child in the world.

Mothers feed the baby first, then do the laundry, clean the house, and use the leftover time to play with the baby. When the mother becomes the teacher, the priorities of the household change. "Playing with the child" becomes the most important job. Mother concerns herself that a certain amount gets done, so meals will appear and socks are clean but not sorted, until sorting becomes a good exercise for the child. The pressure of becoming the teacher is often the catalyst that finally allows a mother to share her homemaking job. Children and husbands usually will only do what they think are absolutely a must. If a mother has taught them that she will do everything, they will let her. As a full-time mother, I felt I had to justify my existence. It is important for me to be there for the first steps and to kiss a boo-boo better, but I felt my mothering was evaluated on the appearance of my children, who were usually naked and my house which was a wreck.

When a parent wants to know what a child wants, the natural process is something like "Twenty Questions." "Is it bigger than a bread box?" "No." While a **closed question** provides a good opportunty for the child to listen, it only provides practice for the words "**yes**" and "**no**" in the child's vocabulary. "Do you want a sandwich?" would be a closed question. The child could answer a closed question with a expanded choice by type of sandwich desired, but would be more likely to answer by nodding or shaking the head. It took significant self-training to shed the parent practice, honed by three previous children, of determining wants through logic and closed questions.

Open questions require thinking, choice and vocabulary. "What do you want for lunch?" is an open question. "What do you want for lunch, a peanut butter sandwich or a Cheez Whiz sandwich?" is an open question providing **modeling and choice**. Reid would answer "nu beur", an early approximation for peanut butter. Then I would ask him, "How do you want your sandwich cut?"

You can cut a thousand shapes out of a lowly peanut butter sandwich or use cookie cutters. I make sandwiches into airplanes, butterflies, space ships, circles, squares, triangles, teddy bears, gingerbread men, cars, rabbits, flowers . . . the teacher takes time for such variety and artistry, because it provides an opportunity for aural training. The child will work hard because he is hungry and interested in the topic. It does not evoke speech until you have learned to use open questions.

Using open questions is not the natural thing to do, because it takes longer. It might not sound difficult, but the exercise is tempered by the desire for information and the child's proclivity to nod or shake his head, showing he has understood the question. The last time I attended Dr.Ling's seminar, we watched a bunch of children manipulate an expert teacher back to closed questions. The children wanted to show how well they were listening and enthusiastically answered with "Yes" or "No," or used their heads, but when given an open question, would force it back to a closed question by not answering. Dr.Ling wanted to keep the children listening so he ended up with closed questions. At home, you are not on stage and if the child wants lunch, he will speak if he knows that lunch comes faster when he talks about it.

Reid has become a most opinionated sandwich eater. He can be difficult when he has told me he would like a "peanut butter sandwich on white bread, cut like a teddy bear" and I cut it in a star. Teachers have to listen too.

The roles of teacher-parent meet head-on over the issue of swearing. At the early age of three, Reid called his older brother a "hamter brain." The children were told it was not acceptable in my house, or in the presence of any adults. That took care of the issue, as far as I was concerned. Ha ha. As Reid's teacher, the issue was more complicated. I am responsible for teaching him all of the language, not just the socially correct language. The "**s**" was missing. Imagine how Reid would be derided, if he were to call someone a "hamter brain." The correct sounds had to be placed as we has placed them in other words which had not been offensive, i.e. "hamster brain."

Now, that he has complete competence in all the ripe and raunchy expressions of siblings and peers the parent has to teach the morals of language. When other children use rude language, they are usually angry and enunciate clearly. Perhaps the child hears this and thinks it is the way of the world.

Reid went to the library story hour and called a little girl "hamster brain" because she was staring at him. Reid does not like to be stared at, but is not capable of saying, "Please do not stare at me because I am just a little sensitive about the fact that I wear hearing aids." In the vernacular, "hamster brain" covered all of that. I was annoyed that Reid was chastised for swearing, but the little girl was not corrected for staring.

You cannot put your head in a bag and only tell children what you would like them to know. In explanation, there is also a chance to inform them about how you feel about an issue. This is even more apropos for the hard-of-hearing child learning all of a language through parental reinforcement. Much of our humor will not be understood unless the vocabulary which goes along with it is explained. If you must take a stand against the use of offensive language, make sure it is as a parent and not as a teacher. If you are the child's prime language teacher, you are responsible for all of the language. If you cannot handle it, find someone who can, like a spouse, sibling, or trusted friend.

We have specialists in our society to teach, or diagnose and treat illness. When a child needs assistance, we look around for the appropriate expert. As we recognize the experts' strengths, we acknowledge our ignorance. The experts, whether they are teachers of the deaf, or speech pathologists, have to spread their time around. It is not possible to have a one-on-one relationship full-time with a professional. One or two hours a week is not enough intervention to insure success.

The experts began to give the parents homework, which increased the amount of time that the child spent learning to listen and speak. The experts suggested, "Practice **ba ba ba** for five minutes". Some parents did what they were told. Probably, many parents made some attempts at practice, but without knowing **why**, did it without enthusiasm. Daniel Ling is adamant that speech teaching should take place frequently during the day, in time frames of two-to-three minutes. To do this, only a parent or prime caretaker is available around the clock.

Professionals must involve and respect the teaching parent as the major focus of the child's rehabilitative team and give the parent as much help as possible. The parent spends hours with the child every day, the professional comes on the scene for an hour or two. The parent asked for help and brought the child in. Professionals should be aware of how profound the parent's drive to help the child can be, and how it is complicated by a feeling of helplessness because of a lack of information. While a parent may feel that something must be done for the child, the parent is fighting to learn all he can. I am less likely to question a professional's competence, if the professional is open and informative with me.

Some professionals will send reports to the school board, the child's doctor, the audiologist, the psychologist and to Santa Claus, but never to the child's parents. Discontinue the professional's services, or arrange to have the files sent to someone who will give them to you.

Experts' reports are not created for the parent's purposes, which makes it difficult when you want outside evaluation of your child's progress. Most professionals spend the first years of their schooling learning a jargon which protects their knowledge from the general public. The jargon is a big obstacle for a parent. A first-year textbook usually contains an introduction to the jargon and outline of general issues. A parent can learn to read an audiogram, or a report of speech development, or a general assessment of skills especially with a little help from a caring competent professional.

What about the parent who does not wish to become the child's teacher? If you are frightened by how daunting it all seems, you must realize that teaching a hard-of-hearing child to speak is a daunting task to every parent who must undertake to do so. You do have options and other people will try to do your job. It will just never be as good as it could have been if you had done it yourself.

Experts' attitudes towards parents is changing. Four years ago, an auditory-verbal teacher told me that I was an exceptional parent because I was at Dr.Ling's seminar. Most parents did not want the pressure. Recently the same teacher said parents were the most useful tool a teacher could have and were getting smarter all the time. We have access to better technology, better techniques, and better information. Of course we are getting smarter. But, it also depends on the experts seeing us as people who can understand and get the job done.

The parents of a hard-of-hearing child become teachers when they have acquired enough knowledge to provide the best possible auditory, speech and language environment in which the child can grow up and have trained themselves to adapt to the vagaries of hearing aids. You understand why you have to do it, and you do it.

Chapter 19
Formal vs. Informal Teaching
of Listening, Speech,
and Language

The demands of Reid's preschool life were confusing. It seemed a good idea to establish formal structured times for everything, to be sure we did what we were supposed to. None of my children have wanted to sit down and do something at the same time every day. Childrens' abilities to experience and to spontaneously learn go on all the time.

Learning When to Listen

Hearing goes on all the time while the child is playing, resting, running, jumping, climbing, swinging, swimming, or eating. Hearing continues even after the eyes are shut, on the way to sleep. Hearing is a major sense. It takes five years for the normal child to ripen and mature enough to go to school. All that time is spent hearing. By school age, the child has experienced a good selection of all the sounds he will ever hear during his life. Without thinking about it, he can hear and determine whether it is necessary to pay attention to the sound or ignore it. If you live in the country and go to the city, the sounds of traffic are overwhelming. The city person learns to ignore the city noises to avoid over-stimulation of the hearing sense. The country person is bombarded with the sounds of tires on pavement, of car engines and mufflers, of trucks, buses and the occasional siren which cannot be ignored.

Hearing should be realized as a major sense for a hard-of-hearing child, and should be continually developed as such. The parent should take advantage of all the sounds of daily life to help the child to recognize that the sound is present, to identify the sound, and to attach meaning to it.

At the same time, developing the ability to hear and **not** listen to background noise is as important for the hard-of-hearing child as for the hearing child. It is a difficult task. As soon as the ear does not hear, it works harder to hear, it strains to hear. It is tiring for the owner of the straining ear. The constant bombardment of sounds is exhausting. This is one advantage for the child who has a greater hearing loss. Limited earshot removes many of the background sounds. The child cannot hear the sounds and does not attempt to listen. The hard-of-hearing child with a lesser loss gets everything amplified into his ears. Practice in the discrimination of sounds has to go on all the time. While the hard-of-hearing child with a mild loss must cope with the same noise as a normally hearing child, it is much more difficult for the hard-of-hearing child who copes by straining to hear and is not as good as the normal child at ignoring background noise. This is why we do auditory training with sounds other than speech sounds. The hard-of-hearing child hearing a washing machine should not have to listen, but should have heard the washing machine clearly enough that he recognizes what it is and can ignore it.

The child should always listen to and process speech rather than categorize and ignore it. (Except for the expression, "Clean up your room." That combination of sounds is never understood by a child unless shouted, causing distortion to the consonants and accompanied by the threatening shaking of a green garbage bag.)

Formal Language Learning

It is possible to train a child to do something by doing it in at a regular time and place. A little child has no knowledge of what a "normal" childhood is, so for that child, sitting down to work for a period of time each day, is normal. Each child has his own personality and so do his parents. There are children who happily sit down and work with a parent for a time each day. The parent has to decide what is best at each age and stage. If you are losing fifteen minutes a day getting the child to sit still, try a less formal approach. You do not have to lose the control of lesson planning, just the reins of when and where it is going to happen. You might have fifteen more minutes every day to actually **work** with the child, rather than **getting ready** to work.

Staying up unusually late the night before, coming down with a cold, being excited by the impending visit of a fat man in a red suit, all these things get in the way of the child's listening and learning. The child has to experience them because they are a part of everyone's childhood. The director of the child's preschool education must be flexible enough to cope, counter and improvise.

Some of the most stressful times have been with Reid in a formal teaching or testing situation, when he has not felt like performing, and Reid has been less than cooperative. I have felt failure as a parent because I could not keep him cooperative. Yet all he is doing is being a real child. Real children do not have time to sit still.

When Reid's teacher came to our house, he would be expected to sit and work for a period of time. In his own house, Reid has security. The variables he had to deal with were sitting down to work and the teacher. Liz was really good at convincing Reid that sitting down with her was exactly what he wanted to do. When we started to go to an auditory-verbal therapist, Reid was impossible. He recognized where we were going, even though I used five different routes to the university. Telling him that we were going to London was asking for two hours of sniveling in the car. Once we got to the parking lot, Reid would dig in his heels for the full fledged, "I am going to be as disagreeable as possible in the hope that I will not have to go in there." Putting money in the parking meter had no charms for him. He did not care about the daffodils at Elborne College. He could be tempted by a doughnut and a coke, so the driving schedule was rearranged so that we always had time. He was even pleased to see Catherine, but he did not want to sit and work with her for an hour. If there were a slide or climbing toy in the auditory-verbal therapist's office, then the children could be rewarded by being allowed to slide and climb.

We had therapy with an auditory-verbal therapist for twenty-four precious hours during his preschool life. Either Ross or I would take Reid, as long as he was healthy. Once I drove down to London through blinding snow and got lost. We arrived forty minutes late. Reid put his head down on the floor and his rear end up in the air doing the ostrich in the corner of the room for twenty minutes. Getting Reid to work that day seemed futile but Catherine and I used the time to chat about Reid's behavior which was as important for me as the language guidance.

Informal Language Teaching

At home, I did not try to have Reid sit still and work. I talked to Reid while our life went on and threw in speech work any time. We sat on my bed to read, but as soon as he had enough reading we moved on to other things. If he was into sand piles, we played in a mountain of sand. Sometimes we built castles together, from blocks, boxes, or the sofa cushions and sometimes he played by himself while I talked to him. We cooked. We shopped. Informal teaching sounds like a haphazard approach to learning a language, but it is how the normal hearing child learns his mother tongue.

Because we were having so much trouble with Barbara's grasp of the reality of what she had said, I was adamant that Reid should learn in the framework of reality. If we talked about a dog, we had a dog handy. If we talked about color, we had toy cars or something that was the right color. Even so, Reid did not learn his colors until grade one. Farm animals are not a problem for country children. Reid knew the names of the farm equipment with wheels before I did. City vocabulary is a problem for country children. Words like "gutter," "sewer," "sidewalk," "street," "lamp post," and "bus stop" are meaningless, unless a special point is made of these things when you are in a city.

At Ling's seminar, Dr. Leeper told us many deaf children do not take a breath before speaking, thus they always are talking on residual lung volume. They simply cannot talk loudly even if they can talk clearly. Blow out a candle. Without taking another breath in, try and tell someone to do something. I made sure Reid was breathing heavily, well, and excitedly before starting to do any speech work. Getting him to fight, or tickling him and laughing, having a tussle, or chasing me up stairs was a good preamble to a good attack on a target. This was another reason why the formal approach to learning seemed too restrictive. "Sit here, learn this." simply does not inspire good breathing habits.

Automaticity

I used the swing set to develop automaticity. Automaticity of a skill is when it can be performed accurately, quickly, with economy of effort and with different contexts i.e. loudly, quietly and with a variety of intonation patterns. The child can produce the word or sound correctly without thinking about it. As the swing came forward I modeled **ba ba ba** (or whatever sound we were working on) and let Reid take his turn to say **ba ba ba** on the next swing forward. We were aiming for a target of three correct repetitions per second, at which point the skill for that sound was assumed to have been learned.

Shopping Centers Are Schools

A shopping center is the best vocabulary expander in the world. There are people and products. Nobody minds if you pick up objects, talk about them and put them back. The background noise is fierce, but Reid learned to cope in the wash of noise which was good practice for the time when he would go to school. I wished for an FM so I could say to him, "Where are you, you little rat? You have disappeared again." When a hard-of-hearing child disappears in a shopping center, you do not get him back by shouting his name. He cannot hear you. Reid usually took off for the toys so I began all shopping trips by going to the toy department so we knew where it was.

Record Keeping

When Reid was first producing phonemes (speech sounds), we kept track of them in a stenographer's notebook, with each sound, word, and the date of use. After a while, this became too much work and a waste of time. It was valuable in the beginning because we knew where we were and could look at the book for our own reinforcement from progress recorded. Once his vocabulary expanded to the point that record-keeping efforts interfered with getting more words, we stopped keeping records.

If you have a tape recorder or video camera, you can take samples of speech for review. Listen to the sample carefully several times, and assess what your targets for the next week are. Tell other members of the family what sounds you are currently working on so they can help too. Over time you will see progress.

Language Learning for All Children

Babies are exposed to language and are said to produce every sound of every human language during the first six months of life. They sometimes even make a clicking that is used by only one African tribe. The give and take between mother and baby reinforces the sounds of the mother tongue and extinguishes the other sounds. Gradually, the baby produces sounds that sound more and more like words. The parents listen for these sounds, especially **ma** and **da** and get excited when the baby says them. Parent and child reinforce each other and speech begins.

When Tiffany was nine-weeks-old, it was Halloween. I said "boo" to her early in the day. She said "boo" to me all day. I phoned my friends with the news that this incredibly clever child was beginning to talk. Sure, she had no conception of why she was saying "boo" on Halloween, but she was beginning to talk. Barbara was a silent baby. She cried, but did not babble. William bubbled and gurgled, but made no attempt at speech. His first word was at fifteen months. He pointed to the Golden Arches and pronounced "Donalds." He did not build up a limited vocabulary, he did not even talk again until after his second birthday, but then he produced full sentences.

Most parents provide correct modeling of the child's language in the natural give and take of a child/ parent chat. The child says something incorrectly, such as 'gog' the parent repeats the correct word 'dog,' the child might repeat the correct word in imitation of the parent, or the child might repeat his mistake 'gog' and play with the words ' goggie, gogga, gogg' or 'a gog.' Perhaps the child is working from hearing a parent exclaim "Look, there's a dog." The contraction in 'there's' removes a vowel sound. The **s** is usually carried forward to the **a**. There is almost a full stop after the **a** which is produced in the throat. Then the tongue must get up to the roof of the mouth to make a **d**. Eventually the process works and the child will get the tongue up. Most babies produce **da,da,da** at an early age, so the problem with 'gog' is not the inability to make a **d**. It is all the incredibly complex sound combinations we use even in a very simple sentence.

A parent talks with a child and teaches him to speak this way. The parent talks, the child listens, the child talks, the parent listens. Most of the time you do not have to think about it, it just happens. When the child is hard of hearing, you still do the same thing, but you must make sure that the child can hear you. Don't talk to the child from across the room. Turn off background noises like radios, TV's, or move away from the noise source. Just talking to the child must always have an acoustical-intellectual override: **can the child hear me clearly?**

When Reid was provided with hearing aids at twenty-one to twenty-three months of age, his speech and language development was assessed as being at the zero-to-six months level by a speech pathologist. She suggested we babble and coo to him, just like we would for a new baby. He had little comprehension of anything we said to him. If he had said, "Don't talk baby talk to me, I am not a baby." we might have hesitated, but his total output of words was **ma** and **ba**. To babble as we had when he had been a baby made good common sense. We knew he had not heard it the first time around.

Talking to a baby is quite different from the language used with a two-year-old child. The baby I was babbling to was a normal, healthy in-quisitive two-year-old. My inclination was to talk to him in commands, "Do not do that," "No." "Get down from that shelf," "Leave the dog alone." "Get out of my bureau." "Stop it." "You are going to break your neck." Probably he benefitted from both.

Speech and language go hand in hand. Speech, according to Webster's dictionary is the act of speaking, involving the production of meaningful combinations of distinct speech sounds. Language is the expression and communication of emotions or ideas between human beings by means of speech. Even though Reid could not talk, nor I would assume, be able to understand much speech, he still had very obvious needs which he managed to get across through a variety of means. He cried, he screeched, he screamed, he keened, he howled, he threw himself on the ground and rolled around, he pointed, he pulled me to a place, and tried to get me to cooperate, or he simply went off and helped himself. He used a lot of body language too. When things were going well and he was happy he was a beautiful, smiling child. He was not happy often. We learned some simple gestures. As I gestured, I spoke. I was told by the itinerant teacher that he would not need to sign, that he would just learn to talk once he got used to the hearing aids. I did not trust that statement because I felt that a child with a mild/moderate loss would surely have better speech skills at two than **ba, ma**, and **wa**. Once we could recognize a speech sound for something for which we had used a gesture or sign, we dropped the visual clue.

I spent the whole day with Reid, and every activity was an opportunity to try and expand his vocabulary. He added **ka** into his vocabulary. I would ask "**ka**? Car? Do you want to go in the car?" He might repeat **ka** or **ka ka.** As Reid babbled a phoneme, I repeated his phoneme, then expanded the phoneme to a word, and repeated the word in a phrase. I worried he might think this strange multi-levelled speech was how he should always talk, but he dropped the lower forms as soon as he had mastered the next one up. We did not make stellar progress. It took the better part of a year to add twelve words to his vocabulary. But we did not ever slip backwards either. One fine day he asked, "Go ka?" True to form I repeated "Go ka? Go car? Do you want to go in the car?" Then I phoned Ross with the news that Reid had used a verb.

Babbling to a baby is one thing. The whole endeavor of developing language needed more foundation than either of us felt we had. Of all of my children, Reid is the least likely to enjoy sitting down and working on a regular basis. Any teaching strategy that had formal work sessions was dismissed as unsuitable. We decided he was going to excel as a speechreader and promoted speechreading by positioning ourselves so he could see our faces. When we found Dr. Ling and learned enough to use it as the basis for Reid's program, rather than hoping our instincts would continue to be right, we were ecstatic.

The Ling Method for Children with Mild Losses

The Ling Method was developed to provide a systematic, naturally-oriented, reference for the development of a deaf child's speech and language. It details the development of speech and language for a hearing child so that children with hearing losses can follow along the same curve, and thus develop natural-sounding, useful speech and language.

By testing and assessment, the child's phonetic and phonologic levels are established.

A basic assumption of the Ling Method is that the children will have the best hearing aids possible, in both ears, and will be using them. A child with a mild loss has a full spectrum of sound available to him, according to the audiograms. Therefore there should be no need to intervene in his language development. However, assessment of his speech will tell you whether the child actually hears as much as he is supposed to hear.

The Ling Method is based on natural language attainment, hence it is very useful for hard-of-hearing children, even though the examples and strategies are of children with severe-to-profound hearing losses. There is an assumption that the hard-of-hearing child with a mild loss can hear everything, which has to be understood fundamentally, but the usefulness of the method is to extract pertinent information about the development of the child's language, rather than how deaf he is. If the child is performing well on assessment, then he does not need remedial work. If the asssessment shows the child has problems with certain sounds, then those are the sounds you begin work with, at the earliest level.

One of the nicest aspects of the Ling method is that it adapts to the ways of children with short periods of work (two-to-three minutes) and a limit of six target areas, so that the child can be successful, not get frustrated and develop language as skills are attained. The teacher has less pressure. Bits of progress are the reward for bits of work. The final, and possibly most important point of the Ling method is making sure that the speech learned is carried over into all communication.

Ling's checklist was the most useful assessment tool we had and provided the basis to Reid's speech and language development. We always had six target areas, four of which he could do easily and two which were a challenge. Slowly, the ticks mounted up the chart and slowly, language began to be a part of Reid's communicative abilities. We always knew exactly what the targets for the week were. Our lessons were inspired by whatever interested Reid. He directed his attention somewhere and I followed right along, choosing the aspects of the interest which might allow practice of a sound or blend. From the child's outlook, nothing could be better. He never has an excuse to be surly, at least not for a long period of time. If he becomes resistant, you just go on to something else, knowing you will get back to the problem one way or another.

Difficult Sounds for a Hard-of-Hearing Child

To teach a hard-of-hearing child a sound he can hear is easy. Depending on the child's hearing loss, he can hear fewer speech sounds as the loss increases. According to Ling, you must use other modalities for sounds the child cannot hear. Reid's audiogram would lead most people to think he could hear anything in his better ear with his hearing aids on. (In a perfect acoustic environment with the sound source close by.) We found by careful attention to what he was saying that he had consistent problems with sounds like **f, th, s, sh, tch.**

We had to teach him to produce a **th** by putting the tip of his tongue between his front teeth, and voicing. Whenever he mispronounced a **th** I looked at him and exaggerated the **th**. There are **th**'s at the beginning, the middle and at the end of words. Exactly how the **th** should sound is additionally complicated by the need to prepare for one of the vowel sounds.

We relied heavily on what I had learned in Dr. Ling's seminar. Take a sound such as **ba**, say it several times fairly slowly **ba, ba, ba**, increase the speed to **ba, ba, ba**, increase the speed to **ba , ba ,ba** , increase the speed to **ba, ba, ba**. Now you are also saying **ab, ab, ab**. Knowing this little trick enabled us to move easily between sounds at the beginning and the end of a word.

F is a sound produced when the top front teeth are pressed against the lower lip. **th** is a sound produced with the tongue between the teeth. The difference between **f** and **th** seemed obvious but Reid was still happily substituting one for the other in grade one. (However, by the time you get to grade one, teaching speech has become an occasional endeavor carried out in private.)

S is a sound produced when the tongue of the **th** is pulled back into the mouth. It was possible to approach the teaching of a **s** by starting with a **th**, but I found it too complicated and used a touch cue. We taught him to produce a **s** when a line was drawn with my finger on his lower right arm, and a **sh** when a line was drawn on his lower left. I tried to be consistent in my corrections of his mispronunciations. Because I was human and used to get tired and forgetful about my enthusiasm for Reid's speech, I would hiss **sssssss** at him instead of using the touch modality. Unless we were in a perfect acoustic environment hissing was a waste of time. Reid did not hear **s**. Knowing this meant we had to place it in every word which had the sound. I often thought we had designed our language poorly if such an important sound was so hard to hear.

When Reid was four, while I was driving one day he said, "Look at the iron on the police car." We had to stop, so I placed the **s** by drawing a line down his arm and saying, "Siren." I told him the big red thing was a cherry or red light and the siren was not on the roof of the car. He put all this information together, said "red light" and asked where the siren was. If I had waited until we got home to do the speech work involved, the magic of the moment would have passed. It would have been more work to place that **s**. Nothing beats visual reality for vocabulary retention, either.

When the child makes a consistent error, say the right word to yourself, and get as close to the sound the child is making as you can. Feel whether your lips are open or closed, what your tongue is doing, if the air stream is coming out your mouth or your nose. My friend, Lars never talks through his nose. I asked his family if he ever had. They all joyously said that they had a family project to not let him talk through his nose. Whenever he did they would pinch his nose. While I am absolutely sure a hard-of-hearing child has a right to grow up without having his nose pinched, we pinched Reid's nose **gently** when he began to speak through his nose. Nasality was a big problem from age three to six. (See Chapter 22).

The Older Child's Speech Still Needs Help, So Does His Ego

Around his fourth birthday, Reid lost his fascination with repetition and frequently shouted, "I sed dat already." My other children stopped repeating modeling at the same age, so we stopped insisting that he repeat my corrections, but made sure he heard them. Nouns and present tense verbs were the first parts of language he mastered, some adjectives and adverbs by the time he was four, but no tenses, and no plurals for a long time. We increased his exposure to vocabulary and other children. We had to learn a new balance between working on his speech and communicating through language.

Reid had an assessment by a speech pathologist every six months, then she retired. Her last assessment showed that Reid was speaking at his age level of four years and the remaining errors were developmental in nature. For a while I thought, "Hurrah, now we are the parents of a child who happens to wear hearing aids." We did not do too much work, neither did Reid. We soon decided that Reid had come along so well because of the work we did with him. At age four-and-a-half, he had not finished learning to talk, and he still had a long way to go. He still had to learn tenses and plurals. He had consistent trouble with the high-pitched sounds like **ss, sh, tch, ch, f**. There are many sounds like this in our language. When we found out his kindergarten teacher's name was "Miss McAllister," we went to work on his rendition of "Mi Mikalter."

We found that most people could understand Reid at age five, when he talked about familiar things. As he was at school every other day, I thought we would work on speech on the days he did not go to school. The reality was that he was very tired, cranky, and needed love, and compassion, and to be accepted for what he was, not continually pushed to improve. We focused less on speech work. We stopped going to the auditory-verbal therapist. We asked the school to assess his speech and language once a year. (We use achievement norms developed for hearing children, not hard-of-hearing children, because he is mainstreamed.) Reid went into kindergarten with "high normal" speech compared with all other children, and at age nine has "low normal" speech compared with all other children. In retrospect, I think Reid was not ready for school at age five.

Once the child can read well, it becomes much easier to correct a wrong sound because you can use pencil and paper. You can pick a private time when the child is in a good mood and do it quickly. I keep a little list in my head and work on the one word which has been obvious. The child now has an intellectual approach to the whole thing, and it is successful. I cannot emphasize the word private too much. The child's feelings and self-image are more important than his speech.

A good informal program requires a knowledge of where you are and where you are going. If you have frequent contact with an expert such as a speech pathologist or auditory-verbal therapist, she can assess progress, and give you homework and explanations. If you are winging it with less help, choose your method and assessment tools. Carry out your assessments on a regular enough basis that you stay on target with the child's development. The child may make no progress or may roar ahead of anyone's expectations. You must always be working exactly at the child's level so that both of you have challenge and achievement.

The child has to know you love him above all else. When you work consistently on the development of language through an informal but targeted plan, in short sessions throughout the day, there is plenty of time for hugs and opportunities for success. When you are not successful, move on to another target which you know is successful, so that the working sessions always end on an upbeat.

Plateaus

When you are really discouraged by a plateau (staying at the same level for a long time) think back two months, or six months. Have you made any progress since then? Regular use of the Ling Five-Sounds Test will tell you if any audiological problems or problems with the hearing aids have popped up. Chances are, the child is forging ahead in another area and does not have the time or energy to do it all at once. Is the child becoming neater with a crayon? Is he learning to tie a shoe lace? While we tend to focus on the speech and hearing of a child with hearing problems, it is the whole child which must grow, not just his mouth and ears. Sometimes progress stops in one area to allow progress in another.

A Well-Balanced Child

It is necessary to enjoy life with the child without always forcing him to rise to the challenge of his hearing problems. We have to be careful not to wreck our children's childhoods by being over-demanding. We are attempting to compensate for a condition which is normal for the child because we consider it to be a disability. He has a right to not listen every once in a while, because that is easier. Parents know more than the child about where he might be going. We have the right to insist that he follow the path we have chosen and that he not expect to be carried when he can walk. It is a very fine line. Sometimes I get it right and sometimes I become apathetic or too enthusiastic. That is because I am still learning about parenting a hard-of-hearing child with each step that I take with Reid. Reading an article about an approach which has worked for a small problem can inspire me to try it out right away, but both Reid and I have to learn before expecting success. Be proud of what you have learned, and proud that you are able to help your child learn skills which will last him for his lifetime.

Chapter 20
Teaching Aids

The cheapest and best teaching aid is your family and yourself, your ingenuity and natural playfulness for hours of talking and listening, every day.

Television and VCRs

Today a kindergarten child is expected to know things which he would not have known before *Sesame Street*. *Sesame Street* provides exposure to the whole world. (Reid called the United States, "Big Bird's country." One time he asked a Customs Guard at the American/Canadian border if Big Bird was around.) Reid preferred TV shows with real people and action and paid little attention to *Sesame Street* or cartoons. We figured out he could not understand the Muppets, because you cannot speechread a puppet. The program required more listening than that of which he was capable. The subject changes were too fast to allow him to process through contextual cues and figure out what was going on. In *Aural Habilitation*, Dr. Ling states that for each time a normal child hears something, a hard-of-hearing child has to hear it over and over. We made a tape of *Sesame Street* so we could watch the same show over and over. The repetition made it easier for Reid to understand a bit here and there. He would put a tape into the VCR and watch one of the old familiars. He grew into watching a "fresh" full hour of *Sesame Street*, when he was almost five. By then, his auditory abilities allowed processing at a sufficiently high level so that each program was not a puzzle with many pieces missing.

Reid watched a tape of *Star Wars* so much that I felt guilty. I could not lure him away to my web of language learning. After a year of wondering how much TV was too much, he delivered, in sync with the movie, every line of dialogue, even using different voices. Now I rent him almost any tape he wants, over and over. He is listening and learning.

Make sure your child can hear the television. Reid always sits in one spot, where he is two-and-a-half feet from the speaker. You might want to buy a patch cord to attach the TV to the hearing aids. A television which a hard-of-hearing child has adjusted to his desired loudness is usually too loud for hearing people. Hard-of-hearing people who have closed captioning available find it wonderful. I am considering adding 900 Mhz wireless headphones to the television room.

Toys

We try to give our children toys they will like and will play with. The child has seen advertising for toys and desires what he has been taught to desire. Desiring is different from having a good time with something, once you have it. A parent pays attention to what the child says he wants, but the parent is interested in enhancing skills with the money spent. Sometimes the parent buys the child a toy because the parent wants it.

My basic requirement for a toy is that it is still playable when 50 percent of it has been lost. I do not buy puzzles and creative projects which only have one possible shape. I find children have more respect for things, when they control what they are making. There is no limit to what they can do, except gross physical limitations which they have to learn about anyway. I resent the assumption by the toy industry that our children are so stupid they have to be provided with molded plastic boxes for castles, or forts. Cardboard boxes, crayons and a parent armed with a good sharp knife are much more fun. From an auditory point of view, the fewer limitations you allow the toy industry to place on your choice of toys, the more you will be able to use the toy in a variety of teaching situations.

A jack-in-the-box is excellent for teaching alertness and anticipation to a toddler, but currently it is not a popular toy. After combing toy stores and garage sales, I found a jack-in-the-box which was not loud enough, dusty and expensive. Reid was close to three, just about over the stage of enjoying such a toy, but I bought it. We had fun.

Every child needs a couple of good building block sets. One year, Santa spent fifty dollars on little toy cars for Reid, to provide a huge set of cars for color sorting and vehicle identification. I held up a toy car saying, "Look, Reid. A black car." Reid replied, "A Zam-Zam." How does he ever get "Zam Zam" from "a black car?" Well, a "Zam Zam" is a Trans Am. I have to read it off the bottom of the car. He could differentiate between all the niftier kinds of cars, like Lamborgini, Porsche, Jaguar, Corvette, or Trans Am. Toy cars should have the type of car stamped on the bottom so mother will look less like a fool.

Reid loved the *Ghostbuster* movies: he turned a school bag and stick into a proton pack and ghostzapper. I bought him the sound and light toy which made wonderful loud noises which he could change (good auditory play) from high to low-pitched sounds. It was played with every day by every child who came near it. For his fifth birthday he got a *Ghostbuster* sweat suit, school bag, hat and proton pack. The FM was decorated with the red circle and ghost. We called it a "communicator." Reid went to school with his *Ghostbuster* equipment and picked up the communicator from his teacher. Was there ever a child so eager to put on an FM? Keep an eye on the child's fascinations. Use what you can to sell something which might be less desirable without enticements, such as the wearing of the FM.

Be wary of talking toys and toys aimed at teaching speech. These toys tend to be expensive. The hard-of-hearing child might not hear what is usually of an inferior sound quality to begin with.

Baking and Cooking

"Play dough'" dries up into little bits and leaves messes. 'Play dough' is purchased infrequently, when I need an afternoon to myself. The first thing Reid does with it, is make something fabulous using several colors.

Then he squishes it all together and it turns the color of floor dirt. You can make your own. Food coloring can be added to a basic sugar cookie recipe to make a modeling medium. The artist's creations can be baked and eaten and there is no mess.

My children started cooking with me as soon as they could hold a mixing spoon, which was about six months. When you allow a child to participate in cooking, don't expect something for the cover of the *Joy of Cooking*. If butter, eggs, sugar and flour went into a recipe, before it was shaped into a turtle, it will be good to eat, no matter what it looks like. The child's artistic creations will not look very lifelike. You have to expect the same thing from his baking efforts. When you go to other people's houses, and they proudly point out the beautiful five-point-star cookies, lightly glazed on the tips with icing, and credit a child, don't feel your child is a nerd because his stars look like amoebas and none of the glaze made it past his mouth. When you are dealing with a child who is hard of hearing, he may feel he gets corrected every time he opens his mouth, it is vital to let him offer his productions, and to praise them.

Preparing vegetables for dinner is another opportunity for conversation. The child is not too good at cutting precise pieces of carrot. It will taste good anyway. Think of the vocabulary involved in a good stew. "stewing beef, cubing, cutting, peeling, frying, turnips, carrots, onions, garlic, bay leaf, rutabaga, parsnip, potatoes, boiling, simmering, water, and wine." Reid is enthusiastic about eating anything he has helped to make. We have two cutting boards and we talk as we go along. Add to your preparation time when a child is involved. When dinner has to get on to the table in a hurry, it is not a good idea to have him underfoot.

Memory or Experience Books

Memory books are created by the parent each day to provide a focus to discuss "What happened today." Memory books are records of experiences and are great vocabulary builders. Stick drawings work fine. Most children are quite accepting of a parent's artistic incompetence.

If money were no object, I would buy a **Polaroid** camera and a truckload of film. I keep my 35-mm camera loaded with prepaid processing film.

Each package of pictures must be looked at in the mall when we pick them up. Reid talks about each picture. Then the pictures go home and are talked about again. Reid likes to go through the "out-takes," pictures which are not put in the books because they are duplicates or there is a better picture. They get thrown in a box. Reid can pull out a handful, or one. He will talk about the picture, with an amazing memory for detail of events of several years ago.

If you have a video camera, the possibilities of using it to build "memory books" is wonderful. You can provide a moving collection of the child growing and you can also create "books" of experiences by subject, complete with sounds. How about fifteen minutes of the child at the zoo, looking and listening to each animal?

Even if you have only a crayon and a little sketch book, you can make memory books which will help in the child's mastery of language by discussion of "where we went and what we did." It is only your enthusiasm which limits how great these books can be.

Michelangelo He's Not

The opportunity for visual expression through drawing, painting and other media should be encouraged and developed. Without a doubt the best artwork my children have done has been on walls which were freshly decorated. The dog is fond of crayons, especially red ones. Never say of a child's drawing, "Oh, what a lovely rabbit!" It will be a horse and the artist will be offended. The correct parental approach is "What a lovely picture! What would you like to tell me about it?" The artist will tell you it is a rabbit. Label the picture so the rest of the family can practice reading. One day you will look at a picture and see a rabbit.

When the children were little, fifteen minutes of painting fun meant two hours of cleaning up. I was tempted not to have paints around, but the satisfaction of laying a good line of paint on paper is great. Caked tempera paints are good because you can control the intensity of color by how much water is added to them, yet it is easy for the very young child to get the bright hues he likes. Buy better quality paper, and quality paint brushes and clean them yourself.

Computers

There are programs designed for language-testing of children with hearing losses, and some designed for self-teaching purposes. We have not used these with Reid. We needed money to buy them, which would mean me going to work, which would deprive Reid of the best teaching situation in the world. I stayed home and we did not have a computer. The first draft of this book was hand written, causing amusement and a strong recommendation for a computer for Reid from Dr.Ling. We saved Grandpa's Christmas checks to the children for three years and bought a computer and programs. We did not buy specialized programs for children with hearing losses.

The ability to review and change written text easily using a computer, makes learning to use written language less of a task for the child. Maria Montesorri said children had to be taught to write and would just learn to read. Will learning to select the correct letter by pressing a button use the same pathways into the brain? Do children have to learn to write as well as to type?

Some computer games such as *Wheel of Fortune, Monopoly, Scrabble* encourage the siblings to interact on a personal level. Anything that does this will help language in the long run. A serious drawback of some computer games such as *Shooting Gallery* or *Brix* and the hard-of-hearing child is that the computer reinforces the tendency of the child to be alone for long periods of time, without talking. This is also true of books, TV, and video/movies.

Where you put a computer, whether off in a back room or up front with the rest of the family, and how you provide seating makes a difference between a quiet solitary pastime and a social interactive one. Our new 486 CD-ROM is in the office, a bright sunny room at the front of the house. We have two revolving and rolling office chairs which fit in front of the computer. Extra chairs can be easily brought from the dining room next door. Someone who needs peace and quiet to do an assignment can close the office door, or work later. Someone who wants peace and quiet to get on the high scores list of the game of *Tetris* is going to have an audience of child and beast. It is not unusual to find six children in the office, especially when we have a new interactive game like *Lost in Time*. It took the whole family a month to work through that game.

It provided lively conversations at dinner, and promoted cooperation among all the children to solve the mysteries.

Books

If you asked twenty people to tell you the titles of twenty books they had found vital in their program of learning to listen, you would have a list of three hundred and seventy titles. Book selection is a personal decision, even for a professional librarian. It always comes down to, "Do I like this book enough to read it to Reid one hundred times?" Other peoples' choices , except Reid's, have no bearing on mine. Books can be used for their interesting pictures, or for their stories or both. You will be reading these books over and over. There are books on our shelves which I avoid reading because the language is stilted, or the story line nonsensical. Before buying a book for a young child I read it out loud. If the book does not read well in the store, it will get worse, not better over time. I spent about twenty dollars a month on cheap books at the supermarket, from Berenstain Bears to dictionary books. Reid's first attempts at changing his voice came from a well-written *Three Little Pigs* which came home with the groceries.

Your public library solves the problem of needing many books. The library might have a story hour. Many public libraries have some services for children with disabilities, such as free access to a toy library, or longer times to keep the books. Be brazen. Introduce the child and yourself to a librarian and ask what can be done for your special needs.

Aural Books

The purpose of the aural book is to teach the child to hear a limited number of basic words. You see the picture, and say what it is, then the child should attempt to hear the sound and to say the word, then he can see the picture. Books suitable for early aural use are rare. Each page should have a clear drawing or photograph of one object on a plain background. The book should have six to eight pages, no more. The aural book goes into the collection of visual books and is the only aural book used until the child has mastered the words. The picture should be something in the child's life. Many baby books have a picture of a bottle, fine for a bottle-fed baby, but meaningless for a breast-fed baby. What is the most appealing, desirable topic for your child? What will make him wriggle with delight as he tries to say the word? Choose words easily audible to the child.

Draw the word out of the book and into the child's world. When it is time for a drink, label the bottle. When the dog comes in, label the dog. Babies learn by repetition. They have lousy memories and even forget their mother. When the baby stops being friendly to the entire world and shows preference for a parent, the baby is developing a memory. The hard-of-hearing child might need more repetition of aural input in order to remember it. The parent must provide the repetition.

There are some limited vocabulary books intended for early readers. The limited vocabulary makes them great aural books when the child is at the stage of using two and three word combinations. These books have between thirty-five and seventy-five new words. If you use books like this at the beginning of the child's listening training, when the child outgrows them, do not throw them out. The child will need them again when he is learning to read.

Literacy

My definition of literacy is simple. When the child sits at the table and reads all the writing on the cereal box, he is literate. When a child is hard-of-hearing, it is possible that literacy skills will lag because auditory skills are lagging. Diane McGuiness in her book, *When Children Don't Learn* (1985) presents a rundown of all the things that can go wrong when a child is learning to read. If you ever have a weekend free, this is a good book with which to curl up. One chapter is titled "The Ear Determines What the Eye Sees." McGuiness says a child must be able to hear, and hear and feel himself say the speech sounds in order to relate them to the written alphabet letters and combinations of letters which represent them on the page. If the child gets incomplete hearing and speech feedback, he will have an incomplete phonic code. I think this work is the crux of why many children with mild hearing losses fail school in grade three. They cannot get to be literate until they have auditory access to a complete phonic code. The child's memory for sounds must be developed through aural training and associations with pictures and print.

As parents of hard-of-hearing children, we must pay attention to the critics of the current cost-effective education system and see what the more individualized means of teaching literacy can do for our children. It is too easy for the child to fail, the system to say, "Well, he is hard of hearing. What else did you expect?"

The more language you can give your hard-of-hearing child to hear, every day, the easier it may be for him to learn to read when he is ready. Books are fine inspiration for a parent who has temporarily run out of original things to say in conversation. Talking to your child and letting him talk is more important than reading to him. When the books come out, make sure that you are comfortable with your choice of reading material. That way, you will put more excitement into your rendition of, "Who's been sleeping in my bed" in a big, deep voice.

Bribery: We Call It Contract Law in Our House

A child who is trying unsuccessfully to do something should get rewarded for trying. It gets complicated with levels of reward for effort involved and raises the question of what "success" should get if "trying" gets one cookie. Occasional bribery might work well to encourage a child to jump over a hump. Generally my children are rewarded with a smile and a hug and effusive congratulations for success. Any first-year psychology student can tell you that an intermittent, unpredictable reward is most effective. I have been known to buy my children candy to shut them up. Parents have to consider their own sanity too. If you do it too often, the child will demand it and might even refuse to perform unless the reward is available.

Take the Child With You

Toys, books and teaching materials are secondary to getting out and doing things. We have spent days in museums, tourist traps, riding subways, going to parks, shopping malls, visiting other people. grocery shopping, and getting shoes repaired. All the mundane little errands and excursions are teaching opportunities for speech and language. Even though it may seem easier to do so, please do not leave the hard-of-hearing child at home with a sitter while you buzz around. Plan to spend more time getting things done, but take your child with you.

Keeping Track of Progress

Various agencies, professionals and educators will test the child. Ask for a copy of any report which is written about your child. You have more right to see a report than anyone else in the world. Parents are the most likely people to see errors in a written report. Many tests are set up with a Pass/Fail threshold to measure progress. The professional does not like to tell a parent the child has failed three targets out of five, but if that is how the test is set up, that is what the report must say. The professional should expand the text of the assessment to the specifics of what targets should be focused on first because they were failed first.

During preschool general skills testing, Reid completely missed all the prepositions: **in, on, over, under, through** and did not discriminate between **behind** and **beside** which sound similar and look nearly the same on the lips. I watched the testing and became aware of his or my omissions. The test results given to me made no comment about the total lack of understanding of prepositions. Extensive, specific and detailed, but easily understood, progress reports make the parent's job easier.

Once a week listen to the child speak and do your own assessment of how he is doing. The easiest way to do this is with a tape recorder. We used real live speech between Reid and another member of the family. You can make lists of speech and language achieved in stenographer's books, or you can use the *Ling Assessment Form*.

Chapter 21
Making Life Safe for the
Child Who Is Hard of Hearing
Without Overprotecting Him

Any child has the right to be protected from all the things mankind has invented to make life easier: but which, when used inappropriately, result in injury or death.

The Telephone. If Only We Could Reach Out and Touch Someone

Using a telephone can be a matter of life and death. Every child should know how to pick up the receiver, dial **911** or **0** depending on where you live and get help. Teach the child not to hang up the receiver after making an emergency call, so the line will stay open to the operator and can be traced even if the child was not understood.

When Reid was three, he would listen on the phone while Daddy or his itinerant teacher talked to him. All male callers were "Dad" and all

female callers were "my teacha Whiz." Other men were amused by the
small voice asking, "You my Dad?" When he was three-and-a-half he
told me Daddy was in the box then looked around for the rest of Daddy
which was too big to fit in the box. That year Reid's godfather called
and said he was the Easter Bunny. "You dah Eastah bunny? You bring
chocolates my hou' yum yum." When he was about four-and-a-half,
Reid spoke well enough on the phone to talk to a friend. "You wanna
com'ovah mah hou' amorrow?" After Reid had finished talking he would
hang up the telephone, rather than listen and talk. When he was about
five-and-a-half he talked and listened.

The telephone does not go over the child's ear, but over the hearing aid,
with the microphone in the middle of the ear piece. Children learn by
copying other people. We had trouble getting Reid to not put the receiver over his ear like everybody else.

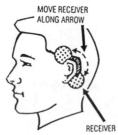

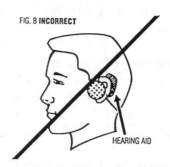

Figure 21.1 Correct Use of Telephone Receiver With Hearing Aid
Drawing courtesy of Bell Canada

Our old telephone handset had a volume control which enabled the user to make the incoming voice louder. Telephone equipment was engineered for optimal performance between 500 and 3500 Hz. and a specified loudness. The equipment had a tendency to distort sounds anytime you change the numbers too drastically in any direction. The alternative was to use the **T** (telecoil) setting and the volume control on the hearing aids. (The telecoil is a electromagnetic coil which bypasses the microphone so the hearing aid user can hear more clearly over the telephone.) Our new VISTA 200 telephone must be plugged in to an electrical outlet. Hence, it uses electricity in larger amounts than the old telephones did. The telephone has a volume control which can get very loud without distortion. Reid does not bother using the telecoil on his hearing aids when he uses the new telephone.

To tell whether telephone equipment is telecoil compatible, look into the earpiece, through the tiny holes. If you see red or whitish silver, or brassy metal, then your telephone should be hearing aid compatible. If you see other colors, particularly black, then you will have to replace one telephone in your house with telecoil compatible equipment, otherwise your child will not be able to use his hearing aids on the telecoil setting. You could also hook up the hearing aid to the telephone, turn the control to **T** and use the stethoscope to listen. Call your local telephone company for more information.

Once the child has some idea of talking on the telephone, he can answer it when it rings and find out for whom the call is intended. One day he will answer, take the message and tell you, "Barba call. She forget lunch for school." He will neglect to tell you that he told the school secretary that you were still in bed at 11:30.

Child-Proofing Your World

If you start child-proofing your house six months before the baby is born, you get pretty good by the time the baby is crawling. Child-proofing is an on-going procedure until the children reach age twelve. Humans keep things handy which are frequently used, such as vitamin pills, or pain pills. Handy for the adult means handy for the child. When a child is sampling medicine by himself, taste does not matter. Accidental poisonings could be eliminated as a cause of death if parents were more careful. A child might experience difficulty opening a child-proof cap, but it is never impossible. The only secure medicine cabinet is one which locks and the child cannot get to the key. Because of the impossibility of maintaining contact with the hard-of-hearing child through the "What are you doing?" call of the parent, dangerous substances must be kept in a safe place.

Yoo Hoo, Where Are You?

When the child is very young, he has no conscience, meaning no aware-ness of good or bad, right or wrong, safe, or dangerous. You are the child's conscience. You must use physical presence to prevent accidents. As the child grows, he develops some discretion. Just calling upstairs can remind the hearing child that, "Mummy" or "Daddy says 'No.' "

One of the things you cannot do to a hard-of-hearing child is shout upstairs when it gets too quiet, "What are you doing?" or "Where are you?", unless you have a FM system. Any hard-of-hearing child does not hear well at a distance and will continue what he is doing until you come and find him. We must be wary of being too heavy-handed with the hard-of-hearing child, because we often react to an undesirable activity without giving ourselves time to cool down before meting out punishment. Hearing children can answer, "I'm here." and leave the scene of the crime. We often catch the hearing child after the fact, because we were reassured by the innocent "I'm here," and did not find the child writing on the bathroom mirror with a lipstick. Then, because we realize that we are at least partly to blame and the naughtiness is over, we tend to be less fierce. The hard-of-hearing child never gets the "Yoo hoo, Where are you?" warning.

Just as the baby learning to walk has to fall, so the child learning to survive, must learn to care for himself and not always have a parent running after him. What happens when the time comes that the parent is not there? Soon after four-year-old Reid was assessed by a psychologist as a nice child with too much mother, Reid found himself out of earshot from his mother. He started to do things expected from a two-year-old, like sticking scissors into an electric socket, or eating the peppers off a hot pepper plant. "Mumm. Dat tastess awful, my mouff is burny,burny." The psychologist had been right. He had not learned not to do things because he never had a chance to try. We had a tough couple of months while Reid learned basic survival. There is an advantage to doing it like this. A two-year-old child has some receptive and expressive language, but complex explanations of why not, go right over his head. At age four, communication is much better. You can rationalize with the child and successfully transfer learning from one situation to another.

The most destructive child I have ever had in my house, broke windows, ripped screens, put bed guards through plaster walls, and ran amok whenever he was not in a supervised, child-proofed environment. Children growing up in such an environment might never learn not to touch, or to handle things carefully.

Occasionally, while driving around, we see a **Deaf Child** sign in front of a house. Ross does not want a **Deaf Child** sign just in case the more twisted members of our society take to honking to see if the child is really deaf, or line up and take aim at the child with their cars. He would allow a **Children At Play** sign.

Bouncin'Up'n Down In Our Little Red Wagon

Parents worry that their child will get hit by a car, especially when there has been a grisly accident on the news. Children get run over in their own driveways, by their own parents. It is never possible to be too vigilant with cars and children. Children spend their lives going places. The car becomes an extension of the house which moves from place to place. They rarely think of getting hurt, hit, or killed. Cars are their friends. A child has no idea that a car cannot stop instantly, or that the bicycle and child are insignificant compared to the mass of a car. It is the parent's job to teach the child to survive in a world full of cars. We began that job very early.

Children belong in backyards, behind fences, and on sidewalks when they want to ride a tricycle, with an adult in constant and nearby attendance. Little children should never be on a driveway or a road. For their seventh birthday, my children get a two-wheeled bicycle to ride on a sidewalk. I take their bikes away when they go through a stop sign, or fail to signal a turn. All the children are vigilant on their bikes.

Traffic is a "look and listen" situation. Hard-of-hearing children can be taught to look. Their visual talents will make them good lookers at an early age. But, what about the "listen?" Both in the car and on the street, Reid cannot understand me when I talk because of all the other noises. On the street, we consider Reid to be deaf. He must hold my hand walking through parking lots, walking down the street, or even on our road. (It has been wonderful to have that little hand always in mine.)

To teach looking, every parent has the same approach: steer the child's head in the directions the child must look. The child gets the idea of looking in all directions. Somehow he discovers he is looking for cars. It takes a long time for a child to develop a true assessment of "Is it safe?" Crossing the street can take ten minutes, but consistent practice with a parent teaches them to really assess safety and not glibly copy what other people do at street corners.

If the child must always stop and assess safety by looking before stepping off a sidewalk, he is more likely to do the same when you are not there and his feet want to run out into the street after a ball or dog, right under the wheels of a car. My dogs were trained to sit at every curb. Once my dog was running after a ball, yet the dog stopped and sat at the curb as the car which would have killed her went by. Certainly, this kind of self-control can be learned by the child through constant training to stop, look and listen.

Reid's play area is as safe from cars as we can make it. I wish we could keep him safely at home, but two-wheeled bicycles and the road will become major attractions. The hearing aids fill with the sound of rushing wind on a bicycle, so that the child can hear little else. We will teach him extra caution, above what his siblings have been taught, because he is hard of hearing and I do not want him dead.

Alarms

The fire alarms at the school for the Deaf are so loud you feel them in your chest. When Reid is asleep, a bomb could go off in his room. I doubt that Reid would wake up to the irritating, but high sound that most home fire alarms have. Even aided, he ignores the smoke alarm at Grandpa's house which, irritatingly, goes off without cause when you have a shower. A smoke alarm designed for hearing people will not be adequate for the child who is hard of hearing. If you are in doubt, take your smoke alarms to the audiologist and ask if the child can hear them. Smoke alarms with flashing strobe lights are available for hard-of-hearing people.

Behind Locked Doors

None of the doors in our house have ever been locked. The children learned a closed door meant you had to knock and wait before opening the door. With a few humorous exceptions this has worked well. It seems that Reid has to check out something with Mom and Dad whenever they try to exercise their connubial rights. Talking through a closed bedroom door to a hard-of-hearing child is ridiculous. When Reid knocks on our door, it is necessary to get out of bed, open the door and talk to him. Sometimes this makes us cranky.

Ross and I agree children should not be locked in bedrooms at night. From the moment they are old enough to get out of bed by themselves, they must learn to stay in their rooms. One night Tiffany discovered she could get out of the crib and came back downstairs. She was an angel with her curly titan red hair but I had just read Dr. Spock's statement about bedtime coming around too often to have a fight about it every time. Dr. Spock said not to be fooled by a charming smile. The child was aware she was supposed to be in bed. The smile was ploy number one. Ross and I decreed in deep voices, "Get back in bed." Tiffany was dismayed that her adoring parents did not want her company, but she went back to bed. This worked fine for the first three children, who went to bed within fifteen minutes of each other. Reid went to bed long before the other children and frequently reappeared to see what could be more fun than going to sleep. We could not control him by shouting upstairs, "Get back in bed" at the first footstep because he would not hear us. After months of constantly putting Reid back to bed, we put a lock on his door.

When Reid was about three, he started to wander at night. He would roam the house until he fell asleep on the sofa with a dog. I cannot understand how a child, who has done everything I have done is not as tired as I am and prepared to spend the night in bed, asleep. I was incapable of providing additional supervisory care for Reid in the middle of the night. The house was child-proofed, the front door locked and the worst he could do was let the delighted dogs into the fridge with him. Reid's nocturnal ramblings ceased when he was about four-and-a-half. Somebody, somewhere, must have studied this phenomenon.

Is the inclination to wander an individual personality trait, or does the absence of sound keep him awake? During the day he wears his hearing aids and gets auditory input. At night he is deaf. Reid has a night light in his room, so night does not represent visual as well as auditory deprivation.

Care of the Hearing Aids and Batteries at Night

Bedtime is when the hearing aids come off and the batteries are removed from the aids. Let me give a word of caution: The batteries must not be left out on a table or dresser or anywhere the child can find them and pop them into his mouth. Establish a safe storage routine from the start. (See Chapter 11 on the dangers of batteries.)

Abuse of Hard-of-Hearing Children

In Canada in 1989, a little hard-of-hearing child was allegedly raped by a taxi driver, on the way to school in the taxi. With no credible witnesses and despite immediate medical assessment, the police would not make charges against the driver. Because no charges were made, the school board did not relieve the taxi driver of his duties. He arrived to pick up the child the following school day. The father went to jail for threatening the taxi driver. The child has gone to counseling at the parents' expense. They had to mortgage their house. Their medical insurance plan will not pay for the child's psychological costs because the child is not in a hospital and no criminal charges were made in the case. The police felt there was little doubt that the taxi driver did it, but "they would have to catch him in the act." The taxi driver has rights, but it is evident the hard-of-hearing child and her parents have none. It might be assumed that they were given inappropriate legal advice by their lawyer and the police. Should this happen to your child, get in touch with a victim's rights organization, or the nearest rape crisis center. In the United States, suspected child abuse must be reported to Child Protective Services by anyone who observes it or has good cause to suspect it.

On a television show **Shirley**,(March 28, 1990) the issue of abuse of people with disabilities was discussed. It was said that 50 percent of all children with disabilities are abused at some point. According to **Victims of Violence** (A Canadian advocacy group) a child with a disability is from **one-and-a-half times** to **ten** times more likely to be abused than a child without a disability.

Be aware that this can happen to your child. Usually there is some element of safety in a group situation. Know your child's daily schedule and who he is alone with on a regular basis. Think about where the child is, for how long, with whom. How well do you know that person? Teach your child to tell you what happens every day and listen carefully.

Ross and I assess many potentially dangerous situations with the wry comment "What would the coroner say?" It is not possible to cover every angle, all the time, but we do our best, beginning with good fences for small children and constant parental vigilance. We hope that by showing the children the things which we have learned to be dangerous, they too will learn, and we will never have to read a coroner's report.

Chapter 22
Temper Tantrums, Whining, and Squirreling

What is the matter with Mary Jane? . . .
She's crying with all her might and main, . . .
She's perfectly well and she hasn't a pain: . . .
I've promised her sweets and a ride in the train, . . .
And I've begged her to stop for a bit and explain . . .
A.A.Milne, *When We Were Very Young*, (1924)

Tantrums

Tiffany's only temper tantrum was over a cookie. I turned my back and walked away. She carried on for a while, then discovered the lack of an audience and stopped. She never tried it again. When Barbara threw herself screaming on a mall floor, I walked away. A stranger intervened, "Here is a candy if you stop making that dreadful noise." Stunned by the interference, I waddled back (pregnant as usual), picked up the child, removed the candy and stuck her, screaming blue murder, in the stroller. From that day on, Barbara averaged five to ten tantrums a day.

We attributed her tantrums to her intense communication frustrations, but the first tantrum was successful. A tantrum was instantly learned and used.

Nothing worked. I read the books, consulted Marcia, my psychologist friend, set up a behavior-modification program. Barbara had tantrums at home, at school, at church, in the car, in malls, and in restaurants. Her last (I hope) tantrum was in grade three. The principal took forty-five minutes to get her to a rational state. Her siblings were embarassed.

I sent her to her room to think. Ross and I pulled her behavior apart. We began with the selfishness of her expectations. We emphasized the unfairness of her actions to her classmates, her teacher, her siblings, and her school. I asked, "Did you choose to scream?" She admitted she had. I said, "Then in the future you will choose not to scream, or find another family who tolerates this." She has chosen not to scream.

Behavior has its consequences. Barbara had a tough time making and keeping friends, because other children cannot be bothered with a child who is antisocial when crossed. As Barbara grows up, she is learning to handle disappointment or frustration better. As she calms down, her genuine niceness shows through. Barbara gives at a high level of love and caring and expects the same.

William had his turn at a tantrum when he was three-and-a-half and going through a late "terrible two's" stage. I asked him, "Do you know how silly Barbara looks when she yells and screams?" He nodded his head in agreement. "Well, you do not look any better than she does." He never tried a tantrum again.

I do not remember Reid's first tantrum. We hoped, at age five-and-a-half, we had seen the last. Barbara had fewer, longer ones and Reid had many short, but intense tantrums. Up to about his fifth birthday, Reid had a tantrum every single time he did not get his way. He was stubborn. So was I. My life would have been much simpler if I bought him every thing he wanted and let him eat chips and cookies all day. Sometimes it was easier to announce that I would buy him one toy car, before going into a store, knowing that I could control the situation by not paying for the car until we left the store. He had to behave well or I would not buy the toy. He still broke the deal when he simply had to have a toy but he did not understand that some toy cars cost one dollar and twenty-nine cents and some cost one hundred and twenty-nine dollars. Actually, neither did I, but I can read a price tag.

Being loving to the child having a tantrum increased the frequency, both with Barbara and Reid. "Look how nice Mummy is being to me while I roll around making noises." After the fact, you can discuss anger, frustration, and distress. You can suggest that the child has an element of control somewhere. While the tantrum is going on, isolation prevents the parent from lashing out in anger and frustration.

A young child may get into kicking, screaming, or holding his breath until he passes out. When there are communication problems adding to the child's immediate anxiety or frustration, the tantrum becomes the child's way out. "Young children with hearing problems, particularly those in an oral approach, have temper tantrums." There must be piles of research documenting this. The parents of "oral" children with whom I have talked about tantrums, have had to deal with them on a frequent and long-term basis. We have been pushed to the brink of our own sanity by this unacceptable behavior. We have tried to understand, to control, to relieve the frustration, to avoid the tantrums or to lessen them. We have often failed and felt like failures because the force of the tantrum and the continual force of the tantrums has worn us out. Parents talk about tantrums. My professionals never mentioned them.

And, as if that was not enough, society comes along and brands our child with other labels besides hard of hearing and discrimination rears its ugly head. In public, I often gave Reid what he wanted, thereby opting for "a spoilt child," rather than allowing him to carry on, even though I knew it would lead to more tantrums.

Hard-of-hearing children like others, respond to what they can see, taste, feel, and think. They are bombarded with attractive stimuli which say "taste me," "hold me," and "take me home." This starts from the moment we buy them the first rattle. The child supposes he has not sufficiently communicated his strong feelings about something. On the second attempt he flips into a tantrum. Sometimes, the first attempts at communication are internal. The child thinks to himself, "I want that . . . I won't get it" and has a tantrum without the parent being aware of his train of thought and wonders, "What on earth has set the child off this time?"

Aside from the emotional complexities of tantrums, be prepared for the physical rejection of the hearing aids and either remove the aids or develop a good catch as they fly across the room. The child must never be punished for this, **it is the failure of the hearing aids to cope with the excessive noise which makes the child throw them away** and not another expression of the child's willfulness. The fact that he is the one making the noise does not matter. It can be very difficult for the parent to always remember this.

Over the years, I have developed a pretty thick skin, but I can truly sympathize when the little child is rolling on the floor in front of the cash register, with a package of gum clutched in his hot little hand. It seems like everyone in the store is blaming you, the parent. Opinions differ on the correct handling of tantrums. No matter what you do, 50 percent of the audience will silently applaud you and 50 percent will purse their lips in disapproval. If it has been a bad day, offer the child to Mrs. Pursed Lips.

Whining

Whining is not as intense physically, but the end effect on a parent can be just as devastating as tantrums. Whining is insidious. In the utter joy of getting the child to talk, you do not realize that he is whining, or mistake it for nasality which you will work hard to correct later, after you have rejoiced in hearing him speak. Then one day you may realize that it is chronic whining and shortly thereafter, you will think to yourself, "Why did I work so hard to teach him to speak?" Reid once spent forty-five minutes in his bedroom, whining away to himself, while I waited outside the door, keeping it shut, anticipating the moment that his voicing would change. As soon as he voiced normally, I flung open the door with a cheerful "Hi, Reid." One look at his mother and the whine came right back.

Whining makes me clench my jaw, slam cupboard doors, stamp my feet and put people to bed at four o'clock. The incidence of whining goes up with the child's tiredness level and is particularly awful when he is getting over an illness. Reid's cousin Eric is also a whiner. His mother has told him many times, "Now Eric, you are whining and sound awful." Eric once tattled to me that Reid was whining. I told him, "You and Reid deserve each other."

You must be sure that you are dealing with whining, a common method of driving parents around the bend and not nasality. Too much nasailty is common in the speech of people who are hard of hearing and deaf. We learned about nasality from several experts at Dr. Ling's seminar. It is often overlooked in teaching speech and language to young children. It resists change the greater the hearing loss and the longer it has been habitual. Nasality is not related to emotional or acquisitive frames of mind. Whining is emotional voice control, nasality is physical. Both are undesirable, but whining is a discipline problem, while nasality is a speech and breath problem.

Hold your nose and say aloud, "I like Ike." Then say, "More men and women." The second phrase is filled with sounds which are supposed to be nasal. The child who is born with hearing loss may not be able to say the first phrase without considerable air coming out his nose. Nasality can become habitual at an early age. It is important that the speech therapist as well as the parent recognize it and provide help before it develops into a chronic problem. Practice with lists of words and phrases which have mostly nasal sounds or have no nasal sounds is easy and effective. Make it a game to try and make a list of words and phrases which have no nasal sounds.

Tantrums and whining are intense and lesser forms of parent control that children like to think they have. Sometimes they do. Parents need a break from these habits while they are trying to teach the child not to do them. You might try trading children with another couple or hire respite care if you can afford it. Siblings too, especially if they are older, benefit from the occasional weekend without the hard-of-hearing child getting all the energy and attention from the parents because his behavior is so unbelievably awful.

At the beginning of kindergarten, after a long day at school Reid was exhausted when he came home. He developed a heart-rending two little sobs, with arms folded across his chest, big tears and head bent. This posturing told us that he was not completely happy. By and large, the two sobs have replaced the full-blown kick and shriek. His siblings are not fooled by the two sobs, "Reid. You're such a cry-baby when you don't get your way." Interestingly enough, Barbara is the one to go over and give Mr. Two Sobs a hug to try and make him feel better.

Squirreling

One New Year's Day we went to a godparent's house for the day. Ten miles from home I remembered that the hearing aids were still on top of the fridge. Ross asked, "Do we go on, or go back and get the hearing aids?" I looked at the kids packed in the back of a compact car and decided, "Onwards. If we let them out, they will never get in again." Reid appeared to cope magnificently without his hearing aids.

About four o'clock he started running in circles around the house, through the kitchen, upstairs, downstairs, around the family room, upstairs, and around the wood stove. He could not stop running long enough to eat a special dinner of fresh lamb, one of his favorites. He ran and he ran, just like a squirrel in a cage. He ran until it was time to leave. He was not upset or emotive. He just could not stop running. We call this behavior "squirreling." We know it is the result of becoming excessively overtired and we believe it is related to coping without his hearing aids, or in bad acoustics. He could or should go to sleep, but he cannot come down from his 110 percent effort of appearing fine even without his aids. "Squirreling" occurs most often out of the house, usually in bad acoustics where listening has been necessary.

The rest of the world does not understand "squirreling." My sister asks, "Doesn't that child ever stop?" I answer that a year ago, he would have had two or three tantrums in the same time frame. "Squirreling" is gentle compared to the force of the tantrums or the insidiousness of whining.

Chapter 23
Guess Who's Finally Invited
to Dinner?

At parent-teacher night, William's teacher commented that William always said, "Thank you," when the teacher was handing out papers. The teacher could have said William was noisy or doing terrific work, but what set William apart from the rest of the class was his politeness. When he is grown up and interviewing for jobs, basic good manners will make the invisible difference. From my point of view, polite children are more fun to take places and more likely to be invited back.

Manners is not just saying "Please" and "Thank you," but recognizing that someone has done something for you. One night during a seminar with Dr. Luterman at the E.C. Drury School for the Deaf, Bob Argal was on coffee klatch duty- a continuous river of small children requesting goodies. No child got a thing until saying or signing, "Please" and "Thank you." One child resorted to a tantrum. Bob kept modeling "Please." The child eventually communicated "Please," and got a cookie. Bob realized the parents were watching. He told us, "Well, they have to say 'Please' and 'Thank you' even if they are deaf." Some parents had decided not requiring deaf children to say "Please" would lessen their demands on the child. Possibly the opposite is true. Not saying "Please" makes the child appear self-interested and greedy. The child might be nice, but the omission of basic manners makes it hard to see. Six month's of "gimmies" are easier to tolerate when the demand of "gimme" is tempered by a "Please." Reid said, "Gimme, ple'." I responded willingly, even though the "little tyrant" stage took a long time because of the limitations of his language.

Parents spend the beginning of a hard-of-hearing child's life wondering when he will ever talk. As we begin to be successful, the child asks for things he wants and answers direct questions. He does not, for a long time, listen. Reid was nearly four, sitting at the dinner table, when the conversation turned to an impending trip. Reid listened long enough to figure out that the dogs and I were not going. He broke into the conversation with, "Am I going to Grandpa's house or staying with you?" This was a significant development in Reid's use of language, because he listened to a conversation and processed it well enough to ask a question.

Our dinner is served at 6:15 p.m. nearly every night. All members of the family are expected to be there. Children are encouraged to debate and discuss without descending to arguing. Other children who have eaten with us are surprised that they are encouraged to speak. One child told my daughter that she liked coming to our house, because we talked at dinner. Her family has two cars and a better house than mine. What they do not have is time together even for dinner. Another child answered open questions with monosyllabic answers and avoided debate. His family eats to survive and does not talk while eating. What will he do when he takes a girl out for dinner? What will he do with his own children? At our table, each child is given an opportunity to talk. The older children tend to monopolize the conversation because they have a broader base of knowledge and can make more valid points. The adult moderates and pushes the younger children into the discussion. Sometimes the younger children interrupt.

Children are not naturally good at assimilating a group discussion and preparing points for themselves, then waiting for the appropriate moment to make those points. Children think that if they use a louder voice, that everyone will listen to them. A fair number of adults think the same way. It is difficult for a hearing child to learn to ride a conversation and even harder for a child who is hard of hearing. The child must listen, think and keep on eating at the same time. He must follow the development of the conversation around the table and change what he wants to say if someone else says it first. Reid has sat at the dinner table from the time he could be propped up in the high chair, as did all the others.

Reid was becoming a 'talking tyrant' at the dinner table. In one of the Alexander Graham Bell Association's newsletters I read about another mother's woes in a similar situation. It was so joyful to have the child speaking that the siblings were told to shut up. Then we realized that Reid was using this as a sly ploy for attention with a captive audience. So we applied the same rules for him as for the rest of the family. He must pay attention, he must listen, and take turns talking.

Every so often I marvel at this child who could, at age five, join in a discussion of David Suzuki's television series, *Nature of Things,*on the topic of euthanasia, with a statement, "You took Cinder to the vet's and he gave her a needle and she died." Reid's speech was not yet perfectly clear, but his ability to use language was stunning. I'm positive that is the result of daily family dinners.

At Beavers (Cub Scouts in the United States), a leader asked Reid what sharing meant. Reid launched into a long story about flying out west, seeing the Rockies and whales. It was not appropriate. Sharing time at school is when the children tell a story. The word "share" came through and the leader's question processed into "What would you like to share with us?" Had this happened at home, I would have realized that he had not heard correctly, stopped the monologue and asked for the meaning again. Home is a place to try things out. It is easy to say, "That is a great story, but we were talking about something else." In public you hope everyone's good manners will ease the situation, that the listeners will listen and the speaker will give someone else a chance.

Guests first! A two-year-old child can handle an unbreakable plate of cookies and offer them around. He feels very important doing so too. Natural good manners make unfamiliar situations easier. If you know how to handle a knife and fork, or how to hold a tea cup, you can concentrate on what is less familiar. For hard-of-hearing children, a thorough at-home grounding makes it easier to go out into an acoustically awful environment and still have a good time.

Restaurants can be nightmares for anyone who wears hearing aids because of the clink of cutlery, the clatter of dishes, the background torrent of voices, fans and Musak. Many adults who wear hearing aids turn one aid off and incline the aided ear in the direction of the speaker. We insist on a table with one side to the wall, away from a dish-collecting area. We ask for noisy fans to be turned off, Musak to be turned down. We explain that we have a hard-of-hearing child who becomes wildly uncontrollable should these things not be done. Usually the restaurant will comply or we do not stay. As Reid gets older he will probably be less enthusiastic about his parents forcing concessions to his hearing problems on restaurants. But he will be so much better at handling the noise that we will not fear he will fling himself onto the floor and start carrying on.

When you are hungry, waiting for dinner in a room that is set up to make eating a sensory pleasure, it is hard to be for anyone to be patient. At home children do not have to sit still until dinner is on the table. Many restaurants have veggies and dip or crackers or breadsticks which help to fill in the waiting time. Varied experiences in different restaurants and practice at home will give the child confidence in any situation.

According to my husband, Ross M. Candlish, the average American family goes out 4.5 times a week. The hard-of-hearing child must learn to survive in a restaurant. Once they have a basis of good manners and an ability to cope in the wash of noise, it is fun. The child must learn the give and take of conversation, the camaraderie of good friends or family, the pleasure of good food, the essence of communication. Without this, there is less reason for all the other things we do.

As part of a **4-H** course on manners, Barbara and Tiffany had to pretend to have a disability during a meal. William joined in by having a developmental disability, Reid decided not to wear his hearing aids, Tiffany and Barbara were blind and a young dinner guest was encouraged to wear ear protectors. The point of the exercise was to enable the children to gain sensitivity and empathy for people with disabilities. The visitor, a talkative teenager, was silent as long as she had the ear protectors on. She could just hear Reid shouting and nothing else. She was fascinated with the concept, but silenced by the experience of her imposed hearing loss. Tiffany had a turn with the ear protectors and did not stop talking for a minute, she just increased the volume of her voice. William and Tiffany had a little tussle while she was wearing the ear protectors. Tiffany said to William, "Aw, you wouldn't hurt a deaf person, would you?" William answered, "Why not?" In the ensuing discussion the children decided that a hearing problem is not the worst burden to be given in life. They have accepted their brother's hearing problems in the same spirit as we have. They are great kids.

Chapter 24
Other Children

Little children need friends just as their parents do. Babies can be amused by other babies until internal demands like hunger, tiredness or "wetness," become stronger than the fascination of a strange looking creature. Toddlers engage in parallel play, meaning they do the same thing at the same time and sometimes interact with other children in the course of play. Toddlers can learn to do what another toddler is doing just by watching and doing. Sometimes toddlers can cooperate on a mutual target, such as building a big sand pile, but they are still largely directed by what they think they want to do and not by the greater goal of a common desire: to build a huge pile of sand. Just as often as you will see two toddlers cooperating on the same task, you also will see one piling sand and one taking it away.

There is no better source of amusement for a child than another child. For a hard-of-hearing child, playmates with colds or sore throats should be avoided. As every parent or spouse of a hearing aid user knows, hearing aids do not work well through a cold because the eustachian tubes get irritated by the virus and histamines, which often ends in acute otitis media and the complications of antibiotics for months. A cold can cause a hard-of-hearing child to miss days, weeks, or months of language learning time.

However, the availability of a potential playmate may depend entirely on the attitude of that child's parent. While your child's hearing aids may go unnoticed in the park, the mall, and even a waiting room, the other parent will go through a decision-making process as to whether he/she wants his/her perfect child to play with your hard-of-hearing child. If you force the issue, there might be problems further down the road. The other parent is probably coming from a background of ignorance about hearing problems, the same position as you occupied before you had a hard-of-hearing child. The parent may be unsure about basic things like "how do you talk to the child," or "what do I do if the child has a temper tantrum," or "should the children be treated exactly the same." These are big questions. You cannot blame anyone for thinking this way. You might encounter less discrimination in a group situation, because no one wants to admit that they are prejudiced in front of other parents.

I was lucky because my niece had a baby boy four months before Reid was born. Reid's best early childhood friend was his cousin, Eric. His mother made up her mind early that Reid's hearing problem was not going to affect Eric. She was not convinced that Reid would learn to talk, but she never told me until after Reid started to talk well. Parenting a hard-of-hearing child is easier when you have one friend who will offer you this kind of support and a child roughly the same age, so you can compare ages and stages without competing.

Eric and Reid do all the things that any two good friends do, mess up the room while roaring around playing cars, building castles, spaceships, swinging and climbing outside, sliding down the stairs, and fighting from time to time. They worked well together on organized projects like making cookies or sandwiches. Eric took over as the speaker while these activities were going on. Eric's speech was plentiful and perfect, which made him a superb role model for Reid.

Eric asked occasionally why Reid had to wear hearing aids and was told that Reid's ears needed some help. Eric was told not to shout at Reid from far away, but to move close to him before talking. Both of these hints presented no problems, even when the boys were three. When Eric learned to ride a two-wheeled bike, Reid was disappointed that it was more difficult for him than it looked. Children with hearing problems sometimes have balance problems which require time before riding a two-wheeler is possible.

Reid did not make any friends at the library story hour, although most of the children there would be in his kindergarten class. Story hour was structured from beginning to end and there was no time to socialize with other children. Day camp was a better place to make friends. There was unstructured time during which the children could play and get to know one another. None of the children at day camp noticed his hearing aids. They considered him to be just another child like themselves.

Reid was not exposed to taunting and jeering until he arrived in the school yard. An older child called Reid a "retard" and "deaf-mute" on his first day of school. Belying my principles of not interfering, I phoned the principal and suggested this ignorant child be stopped. The principal spoke to the child. I happened to meet the child in the grocery store and explained the meaning of 'deaf', 'deaf-mute' and 'retard' to him in a carrying voice. He has left Reid alone, but terrorizes all my children by threatening to run over our dog with his ski-doo. Life goes on.

Much to my dismay, my children fight with each other. The boys tussle with their friends and create havoc in the house. I'm convinced this is why the British sent their children away to school. Their antique houses could not take the destruction. Ross assures me this aggressive, destructive behavior will end when the children get friends of the opposite sex. Until then we have passed a law which says, "Go outside, away from the adults, fight and get it over with."

William wins by sitting on Reid, but Reid gets his fair share in too. When Reid thinks he is losing, he starts bellowing and crying. William is reminded that he outweighs Reid by fifty pounds and is capable of killing him. The adults outweigh William and are capable of revenge if he takes advantage of Reid. To quarrelsome children I say, "Think of me as the Secretary-General of the United Nations. There will be peace or there will be no peanut butter." The allegiances change from day-to-day, which is the only saving grace to the children's altercations. They cannot mean what they are saying because yesterday the enemy was a best friend. They are like puppies in a pile trying out their teeth, and practicing how to defend themselves.

It is difficult with such a physical difference between William and Reid, an age gap of five years. The tendency is to protect the "baby," but the baby can really hurt when he punches or bites or hits. When the odds are more even, such as Reid and Eric, I do not interfere, except to take away the hearing aids.

One of the major differences between living in the country and the city is that friends stay overnight. It has its advantages though. Children who have slept at your house tend to be friends forever. Even if the children do not hit it off as well as was expected, your child gets a good grounding in being pleasant and a good host to everyone and not just to best friends.

Asking a child to spend the night is a way to handle a bully at school. After spending a night in your house and doing things with your child, bullying tends to stop. The bully is on shaky ground while your child is on familiar home turf. You can see whether there is a true bullying relationship, or the children are deciding how to be friends.

Usually "sleepovers" are not a good idea with preschoolers because the child needs the regular going-to-bed routines with his parents and his own securities. It is a major step to cope with going to bed in a strange house. John, a ten-year-old visitor was so distraught that we drove him home, (twenty miles in the middle of the night). The next time he came, John was able to cope because he knew we would take him home if he wanted to go. John has moved many times and has little security in his house. His parents are a constant for him and he needs them at bedtime.

When your child is young, you can pick out some friends for him, and he will be happy with your choice. By kindergarten, your choice is gone. The child will be friends with the children he feels drawn to. Reid's first friend that he chose for himself was a tiny hyperactive boy in grade one who was not a good speech model. Reid did exactly what his friend did while parents and siblings watched in wonder.

Mikey's mother is a speech pathologist, and my friend. Mikey and Reid get together to play on those rare occasions when both boys are healthy. Mikey and Reid play together nicely. One day when we were visiting, Gay overheard Reid correct Mikey's incorrect "mans" to "men." Mikey repeated, "men" correctly. Reid put his hand on Mikey's shoulder and said, "Good boy, Mikey." The two friends went on with their day.

It is lucky to find another child with the same hearing loss as your child has. The parents can draw inspiration from each other. The children might help each other sort out the things that we cannot help with, because we do not wear hearing aids. Whether the children choose to remain friends has to be their decision. We cannot force a friendship based solely on the fact that two children wear hearing aids. They might not like each other at all. You can only provide the opportunity through parent organizations like **Voice for Hearing-Impaired Children** or networking in your community.

Friends become more important as the child grows. By about age twelve, friends have more influence than parents in many ways. Parents provide the security, teachers fill the minds, friends are for fun. Reid's move into the world of his peers is not much different from the moves made by his siblings. He does not see himself as different. Whether his friends do or not will depend on Reid's personality, not my intervention.

Chapter 25
Off to School

Raising a child is a testament to blind love. The bond of love between parent and child is unchangeable. We love our children all the time. Even when we do not like how they are behaving, we still love them. If we lose a child, through death or divorce, we grieve. Babies learn that someone loves them so much that their wants and needs will be satisfied. Harlow's monkeys, which had a wire-frame "mother" and a bottle for nourishment, were sickly and antisocial, and showed evidence of brain damage. The control group of monkeys, which had real mothers, were healthy and grew up to be normal monkeys. One conclusion we can draw from this study is that children need love as much as they need food. Children with special problems need an extra dose of love and acceptance. Their parents must provide this and they need informed help from the time that the child is born.

As my children toddled off to kindergarten, I was sad because they were going into an impersonal environment. The school system may tolerate children, and may even like them, but no one at school loves my children the way their family does. Yet, at the same time, the child gradually turns away from the perfect accepting love which the parents offer, and chooses the fickle love of the peer group, the anguish of the crush, the dating game, and, eventually, the love of a spouse. This is part of growing up, to reach beyond the love of the parent to find love in the world.

The transition from loving home environment to the challenges of schooling can be difficult for children who are hard of hearing and mainstreamed, yet still need extra help. Their problems may not be understood. They may seem badly-behaved or retarded. They may be frustrated by communication problems and thus angry and exhausted, and may find their new world a hostile and unhappy place. **No child or adult knows what he or she does not hear**. Children who are hard of hearing must learn to repeat what they hear, to process and to question immediately without recrimination for getting it wrong or interrupting, both at home and at school. For many children who are hard of hearing, listening and writing, or lipreading, and writing at the same time are difficult challenges.

Today, school budgets often are stretched to the breaking point and do not permit much extra equipment or training for teachers. Large classes and overworked staffs make it difficult to provide an effective education to children who have hearing problems, especially those with mild losses. What schools offer in the way of resources for mainstreaming children who are hard of hearing varies within each school system, whether it is state, province or county. What it boils down to is the individual school, the individual principal, and individual teachers. Money must be allocated by each board for training teachers in mainstreaming, for physical equipment, such as personal FMs or sound field amplification as well as classroom acoustic decorating (rugs, draperies and sound baffles). It all goes back to the basic notion of love. We love our children. We would do **anything** for our **own** children that would help. The school has to spread its resources over many children, and furthermore, the school board often may dictate policies without even looking at the children that they are affecting.

The teachers could make life easier for themselves if they would start to think of parents as resources. Start educating yourself to educate your child's teachers. Collect short articles that are easily understood and pass them along to the teacher, beginning with the "**Useful Tips 5: To Share With Caregivers, Family Members, Teachers, and the Outside**

World" at the back of the book, (see p. 218). The whole section of **Useful Tips**, categories **1** through **10** might prove helpful. Suggest teacher training, and keep yourself up-to-date too.

Keep your child's hearing aids in peak working condition, and keep a supply of fresh batteries at school and at home. Make sure the FM is being used at school by dropping into the school unannounced every so often. See your audiologist as often as he or she recommends.

Dr. James MacDougall of McGill University told me that school was often hard for children with hearing problems, because we are asking them to do things that are difficult for them. Once they are through school, life becomes easier because **they can choose what they want to do**. School aside, Reid's future will be based on his ability to speak and comprehend spoken language. No matter what, he will always be able to listen and talk to his friends, his teachers, his boss, and his family because of the love and support his parents and his siblings gave him during his preschool years. This support will continue. We have shown in the first twenty-four chapters of this book how we prepared Reid for his first day at school and his school future. In addition, we have told you all the big and little things that can make such a difference for your child who might have a hearing problem by telling you about my child, our successes, and our stumbling blocks. Long ago, Socrates said. "There is only one good, knowledge, and one evil, ignorance." This is still true today. A parent who has a child with a hearing problem can counter the ignorance that still pervades our modern information-based society by acquiring enough knowledge to stand up for the child, become his or her advocate, and be the best parent possible. In the long term, it really doesn't matter that the child has a hearing problem because you can learn to live with it. All those strange routines become automatic, and the child matures as you do. The child's need for loving, supportive parents will continue in all the child's roles. You have to be there behind the child, armed with calm, confident knowledge.

What I said at the beginning, I repeat, the child who is 'Not Deaf Enough' can fall between the cracks so easily. He or she has learned to cope too well with the problem until the problem has become indeed invisible.

Finally, in this chapter we have described the transition from the sheltering, loving world of the home to the real world of the school. We have mentioned some of the problems the schools have in today's world and we have given a few suggestions on what parents can do to make life easier for both their child and his teachers. Most important, we have shown some ways in which you can play that most essential role: your child's advocate.

Thus Reid's preschool life concluded, with a giant step into the future in the company of his friends and his siblings, Tiffany, Barbara and William and a confident wave to me through the window of the yellow school bus.

Figure 25.1 Off on the School Bus
Photo by PAM Candlish

Useful Tips and Thoughts

1) On Early Diagnosis

1) Early and accurate identification of hearing loss is essential because there is a critical learning period for best language development. Babies need to hear from birth in order to build a memory of what they hear. (See Rubin, 1993)

2) Prenatal and Early Infancy Indicators for hearing loss:
   A. There is a family history of hearing loss.
   B. Their mothers had viral or other non-bacterial infections during pregnancy such as rubella, herpes, syphilis, etc.
   C. There are abnormalities of the head, face, or external ears.
   D. They have birth weight less than 3.3 lbs.
   E. They contract bacterial meningitis.
   F. They show high levels of bilirubin.
   G. They have severe asphyxia, coma, seizures or the need for continued ventilation. (Martin, 1991)
   H. They were admitted to Newborn Intensive Care for more than five days.
   I. They had APGAR scores of below 4 at 1 minute and below 6 at 5 minutes (newborn vital signs measured at birth).
   J. The mother had ingested drugs or alcohol during pregnancy.

3) If the baby does not seem to alert to loud noises close to the ear, start checking for the possibility of hearing loss.

4) During the first six months all babies babble and make **all** the speech sounds. Check the vocal sounds the older baby makes when babbling and compare them to charts of normal speech-sound development.

5) If you think your child has a hearing problem, persist in getting an early and correct diagnosis. The parent is usually right.

6) Get a second opinion if the professional thinks there is **no** problem but you are sure there **is** a problem.

7) See an audiologist as soon as possible and discuss the need for a Brainstem Auditory Evoked Response (BAER) Test.

8) Get hearing aids on the baby as soon after birth as possible.

9) Children of all ages who have hearing problems often have a high proportion of middle ear infections.

10) Signs of Hearing Problems in Early Childhood

A hard-of-hearing infant may indicate his/her hearing loss by various signs at various periods of his/her infancy.[1]

A. Zero to six-months. A hard-of-hearing baby may have:

1) No response to sound by startling or withdrawing.

2) No awareness of location of sound by turning head.

3) Loud crying, excessive crying, no crying.

Babbling is not a guarantee of normal hearing; most babies, including those with a hearing loss, babble in the first six months.

B. Six to twelve months. A hard-of-hearing baby might:

1) Reduce babbling or lack a variety of sounds, the classic symptom of hearing problems.

2) Limit babble to labial sounds which the baby can see.

3) Limit babble to lower, easily heard sounds such as **ah** and **oo**.

4) Look for visual cues and get more involved in complex pictures than expected.

5) Become good at feeling vibrations from footsteps and will learn to anticipate someone's approach from such feelings of vibrations.

6) Anticipate by time of day.

7) Have little interest in speech, will not turn head to listen.

8) Remain unresponsive until he can see you. Many parents call this being "like a rock."

9) Choose toys which are tactile or visual, not auditory.

10) Sleep well, not roused by ordinary household sounds.

11) Move mouth, but make no sound.

12) Have loud cry, loud voice.

13) Not respond to sounds such as a knock on the door, doorbells, or mother's voice from outside the room.

14) Not respond to word "No," but understands gesture or nodding.

15) Never vocalize.

[1] A. *How Does Your Child Hear and Talk?* (1986) **NAHSA** pamphlet. Bethesda, Maryland.
B. *Signs of Hearing Loss.* (1989) **Unitron**, pamphlet E89-03, 520-032-000.
C. *Your Baby's Hearing: A Booklet for Parents.* (1976) **Canadian Hearing Society, University of Colorado Medical Center, Auditory section, Listen Foundation.**
D. Parent observations and comments in interviews.

C. Twelve to eighteen months. A hard-of-hearing child might:

1) Appear to not listen.

2) Be unaware of parent's voice from another room or behind the child.

3) Move closer to sound sources.

4) Ignore toys which he cannot hear.

5) Have an unpleasant voice.

6) Be erratic, with no sense to what he hears.

7) Would be able to anticipate by time or habit.

8) Not locate sound.

9) Not try to attempt to talk.

10) Not be auditorily in touch with the world.

11) Not find sounds exciting or meaningful.

A toddler should have at least two-to-three word vocabulary at twelve months, eight-to-ten words at eighteen months.

D. Eighteen to twenty-four months. A hard-of-hearing child might:

1) Not be starting to form two or three word sentences, or questions.

2) Not use language as a tool. A normal child includes speech when happy or upset, is capable of saying "no-no-no" and crying, a hard-of-hearing child cries without words.

3) Not have a soft voice.

4) Have difficulty with two-part instructions, unless he sees the parent's face.

5) Screech and have a high-pitched, loud, unpleasant voice.

6) Turn up sound too loud on radio, TV or CD, after learning use of volume knobs.

7) Be unaware of TV sound, radio, or music.

8) Consistently not come when called.

9) Appear more than normally absorbed in whatever he is doing, not easily distracted by sound.

10) Be easily distracted by visual stimuli.

11) Develop alternate strategies to cope which may be so good that he appears to hear, when he does not.

A child of eighteen to twenty-four months may have a ten to fifteen word vocabulary.

E. Two to four years. A hard-of-hearing child might:

1) Not ask permission before doing something, but go ahead and do what he wants.

2) Not be able to point to familiar objects when asked.

3) Not be interested in speech, or environmental sounds.

4) Be very visual.

5) Appear unresponsive, self-centered, retarded or autistic, withdrawn from the world.

6) Have some speech, built on labial sounds, such as **ba ma wa pa fa va** which he can see (i.e. read on peoples lips), or low frequency sounds which he can hear. Not all children with hearing problems have a profound hearing loss, something parents tend to forget when they observe their child.

7) Hit or cry, rather than talk, and not behave nicely to other children.

8) Have an ugly, unpleasant, loud, screeching or screaming voice.

9) Cry very loudly or voicelessly.

10) May be able to produce only the sound of laughter.

11) Have many tantrums in the course of a day.

A child of two to four years develops a vocabulary of two-to three-hundred words and uses two-to-three words in sentences. As the child grows, language becomes more complex and varied. Language becomes a tool to get what the child wants.

F. Four Years and Above An older child with hearing problems might:

1) Have difficulty paying attention in school.

2) Have problems understanding someone if he or she is behind him when talking.

3) Seem to hear only when he or she wants to hear.

4) Seem to speak too loudly.

2) On Raising a Child Who Is Hard of Hearing

In General

1) Hug your child who needs extra love and encouragement. Give special hugs to reward success.

2) Let the child enjoy life. Don't require listening and speaking tasks all the time.

3) Be sure the child's siblings understand his or her problem and how they can help.

4) Use help from friends and family. Find ways to streamline your daily routine in order to make time to teach language development.

5) Take your child everywhere: subways, parks, shopping malls, grocery stores, etc. are all teaching opportunities for speech and language.

6) Pay special attention to your hard-of-hearing child's appearance. It is important to have the child suitably dressed for peer approval.

7) Downplay the fact that your hard-of-hearing child has to have more parental attention and money spent on him or her for earmolds and hearing aids by taking all the children shopping separately from time to time.

8) Always have your child wear his or her hearing aids, except in high winds and pouring rain.

9) A child who is hard of hearing may appear to be slow or even retarded. Although he or she can hear at a distance, it takes more time to integrate and understand the message.

10) Teach your child to repeat what he hears, and to question what he does not understand.

11) The child may feel that it is unfair to be hard of hearing, but you can let him or her know that you are providing the best help and technology you can to compensate.

Talking to Your Child—Earshot and Noise

1) Talk to your child *within earshot*. Find out from your audiologist the exact range of earshot for your child.

2) Squat down when you speak to a small child. Sit on a low chair close to the child or take the child on your lap.

3) Never Shout. Shouting distorts speech sounds. All hearing aids have a built-in sound suppressor which automatically cuts off the too-loud noise.

4) A whisper from three inches in the hearing aid is louder than a shout from sixteen feet.

On Improving the Hearing Environment

1) Understand the conditions which make it difficult for a child with hearing problems to hear; then create the best acoustic environment possible so that learning to listen is easier.

2) The sounds your child can hear in the real world are not exactly like those on his audiogram which is the result of testing in a perfect acoustic environment. (Add about 30 dB to his threshold.)

3) When decorating the rooms in which the hard-of-hearing child spends a lot of time, soft materials and fabrics absorb sound and extraneous noise.

   A. A ceiling of acoustic tile rather than a flat, hard, painted surface.

   B. Drapes rather than venetian blinds.

   C. Rugs and carpets rather than a bare floor.

   D. Corduroy or velvet cloth over tables.

4) Most sound systems can be modified to give pleasure to a child who is hard of hearing. Be very careful not to damage the child's residual hearing by turning sound equipment up too loudly. Generally the volume dial should never be turned above half-gain.

5) Ask the child what he or she thinks can improve his or her hearing environment.

Teaching and Learning

1) Learning and hearing go on all the time while the child plays or rests, runs, jumps, swims, and eats. Keep talking while life goes on: cooking, playing in the sand pile, reading, so that he or she can learn language in the same way that a hearing child learns his or her mother tongue.

2) Take advantage of all the sounds of everyday life and get the child to recognize that a sound is present, to identify it, and attach meaning to it. Discrimination of sounds goes on all the time. The child must hear the dishwasher, recognize it and ultimately, ignore the sound.

3) Match vocabulary to what is happening at the moment or what is visually apparent: if the dog comes into the room, talk about dogs. Let the child's own interests inspire the informal learning sessions.

4) The child who is hard of hearing needs more repetitions of a word in order to remember it. The repetitions should be spaced out over time and as opportunities present themselves to use new words.

5) Children who are hard of hearing are so accustomed to listening and coping that they ignore the sounds that they can't hear or interpret, and cruise through their childhoods until the teacher demands singular or plural endings or past tenses in written work.

6) Don't make small children sit still for long, formal daily learning lessons; instead have short, informal sessions. (Ling recommends two or three-minute sessions throughout the day.)

7) Assess your child's speech regularly so that you stay on target with his or her development. Make lists of speech and language achieved in a stenographers notebook or use the Ling Assessment Form. You may find it useful to use a tape recorder or video camera to record speech progress in order to plan targets for the next week.

8) Do not be discouraged by what seems to be a lack of progress. This may be the result of:

   A. Inappropriate goals or lack of identification of steps to reach the goals.

   B. A child/parent/therapist signal for a change of procedure.

   C. The child may be progressing in another area, i.e. physical activity, game mastery, and have no energy to work on speech.

   D. The child may be accumulating skills and waiting to achieve a certain level before using them.

9) Home programming from professionals should be clear with one or two attainable goals. There is no such thing as failure. Failure just means postponing this week's goal to next week.

10) Always end a teaching session on an upbeat note. When you are not successful, end with a target you know will be successful.

11) Reading skills lag in the majority of hard-of-hearing children. A child must be able to hear, and hear and feel himself say the speech sounds in order to relate them to the alphabet letter and combinations of letters which represent them on the page.

12) Children with hearing problems may also have balance problems, which may be noticed when they learn to ride a tricycle or bicycle, or use a diving board.

13) Children with hearing problems may also be clumsy children. Usually the clumsiness is outgrown, but not always.

14) If you do not actively teach language to a child with a mild hearing loss he will not automatically learn speech.

Manners and Social Situations

1) Natural good manners, grounded thoroughly at home make unfamiliar situations and awful acoustic environments in the outside world more manageable.

2) Teach the child who is hard of hearing how to take part in normal dinner table conversations: how to pay attention, to listen, and take turns talking.

3) Let the child take part in family social occasions: Let him or her pass cookies or finger foods to guests.

4) Make sure that the child has the opportunity to overhear all the conversations. If he or she has missed part of a story, fill in the blanks for the child. Make sure that the rest of the world is as polite to your child as you insist that he be.

5) In restaurants, try to get a table with one side to the wall, away from the dish washing area. Ask for noisy fans to be turned off, and Muzak to be turned down when possible.

Friends and Playmates

1) Small children learn by doing as other children do. All children need friends.

2) It is great for your child to have a friend with the same hearing loss. Both the children and the parents can help each other.

3) Beware of a playmate with a cold or sore throat. A cold can cause a child who is hard of hearing to miss days, weeks, or months of school and language learning time.

4) Do not be surprised if parents of hearing children may hesitate to let their children play with a child with hearing problems. They may feel that they would not be able to handle the problems.

Obnoxious Behaviors

1) Do not talk while the child is talking because he or she will not be able to understand or remember what you are saying. The sounds the child is making will drown out the sounds you are making in the hearing aid.

2) When the child is screaming or crying, he or she cannot hear anything. Wait until he or she is quieter and calm the child by hugs or touching and stroking.

3) Children with hearing problems may have tantrums out of frustration at not being able to communicate.

4) When the child has a tantrum, isolate him or her.

5) Children with hearing aids currently having a tantrum cannot stand the sound of the noises they are making, so they pull the hearing aids out of their ears and throw the hearing aids away. Either grab the hearing aids first, or develop a good catch. Do not ever punish a child for throwing the aids away during a tantrum.

6) Be sure you are dealing with whining, which is an emotional and discipline problem.

7) Take a break from tantrums and whining while you are teaching the child to eliminate them. Let friends or family take the child for a few days. You will benefit. So will the other children in the family benefit from your undivided attention.

8) If your child is badly behaved at a hearing test or any other visit to the many professionals involved with a hearing loss, think how hard the child has to work when he or she would rather be playing.

9) Put a night light in the child's bedroom so bedtime is not visual as well as auditory deprivation.

3) For Parents

1) Both parents should attend hearing tests, then both will be accurately informed. Both parents should hear the diagnosis from the professional.

2) From the beginning get as much information as you can. Read and ask questions of all your professionals, doctors, audiologists, speech professionals, teachers, and psychologists.

3) Get information on hearing problems to identify your child's problems and to learn how to help. The public library is a good place to start.

4) If possible attend seminars and/or workshops about hearing problems.

5) Get help from organizations such as the Alexander Graham Bell Association for the Deaf, American Speech-Language-Hearing As-

sociation, John Tracy Clinic, National Information Center on Deafness at Gallaudet University and Self Help for Hard-of-Hearing People.

6) Parents of children with hearing problems should help each other, and pool their knowledge, regardless of the degree of deafness of their children.

7) Be encouraged. Think through the limitations of the child's hearing problems and train yourself to live within those limitations. It is easier than you would think to cope with a child who is hard of hearing on a day-to-day basis, once you have good technical information and a little experience.

8) Seek information and experiment. It is normal to be confused. If you are getting conflicting information: Mull it over; talk it over. Try one approach, but don't be afraid to try another.

9) Don't dwell on why your child has hearing problems. Concentrate on what you can do now to help the child for the rest of his or her life.

10) A normal life in the hearing world is becoming more attainable for the hearing impaired with the endlessly, ever-improving technology. Inventors are coming up with new improvements every day. At present, a child who is hard of hearing can grow up to function in the hearing world, even though he or she will always be hard of hearing.

11) Hearing aids help, but do not cure hearing problems. The child will work hard to listen and should be educated to speak and lipread.

12) Children with mild and moderate hearing losses need parental advocates to protect them.

13) Be patient and be proud of progress. It is good that you are able to teach your child skills that will let him or her have a normal happy, and productive life.

14) Hug your child with hearing problems. He or she needs lots of love and encouragement.

15) Hug your other children too.

Parents As Teachers

1) The parent of a child with hearing problems must become a teacher. Speech learning sessions should be done frequently in short, two-to-

three minute sessions throughout the day. Parents or prime caregivers and family are the best teachers because they are available, and love the child.

2) Parents become teachers when they acquire enough knowledge to provide the best possible auditory, speech and language environment.

3) Your first priority is to have enough learning time with your hard-of-hearing child. Let the housework go and get the family to help with household chores.

4) Teach the child the proper speech sounds, even for rude and raunchy words. You, as a teacher have to teach the child to say the word correctly. You as a parent have to teach the child never to say the word.

5) Parents and siblings are the best teachers a child with hearing problems can have.

Day Care Centers or Camps

1) Inform them about your child's hearing problems and proper use of equipment. Drop in unannounced. If the child is not using the equipment, change centers.

4) On Choices in Deaf Education

1) **Oral Education or Deaf Culture** or somewhere in between. The choice depends on the child, the parents, and the services available locally. All parents want a happy child who grows up into a happy adult. It only seems fair to give all children with hearing problems a chance to learn to listen and speak and become part of the hearing world. Hearing problems are viewed as a disability in the hearing world while hearing problems are viewed as a difference in the Deaf culture. Parents and teachers want what is best for the child, but the choice can be agonizing. Few children with a mild or moderate losses will gravitate toward the Deaf culture.

2) **Oral Education:** A system for those who are hearing impaired that teaches them to use whatever hearing that remains to be amplified by technology. (hearing aids, FM systems, cochlear implants)

3) **Speechreading:** The ability to read the shapes of speech sounds on the lips.

4) **Deaf Culture:** Those Deaf people who define themselves as a separate culture whose primary characteristic is the use of American Sign Language. ASL is a full language capable of expressing any element of human thought.

5) **Sign Languages:** Communication systems using visual hand signals and gestures exclusively.

6) **Fingerspelling:** A visual system which uses codes for twenty-six letters and ten numbers. Fingerspelling is used within sign languages for proper names.

7) **Cued Speech:** A method which uses gesture to partially replace some hard-to-see speech sounds. Eight hand shapes represent groups of consonants sounds and four positions around the face represent vowel sounds. Combinations of hand shapes and placements show the exact pronunciation of words. Cued speech can be explained in a few hours.

8) **Total Communication:** This involves speaking and signing at the same time.

5) To Share With Caregivers, Family Members, Teachers, and the Outside World

1) Learn to talk to and understand the child, and listen when he or she speaks.

2) All prime caregivers, family, teachers and babysitters must fully accept and deal with the child's hearing problems, or the child will not be safe with them.

3) Parents and caregivers should go to the hearing aid dealer or audiologist so they will be taught by a professional about hearing aids and hearing problems.

4) Music, air conditioners, some computers, refrigerators, vacuum cleaners, dishes clattering in a sink, and other people talking. Listen to these background noises which you normally ignore and try to eliminate them in the world of a child with a hearing loss.

5) Speak to the child within earshot, usually within four to six feet.

6) Be sure that you have the child's attention before speaking. Be sure that your face can be seen clearly. Don't talk behind the child or to one side. Don't put your hands in front of your face. Try not to chew gum, eat or smoke when speaking.

7) Never shout at the child.

8) If the child does not understand you, use another word. Repeating the same word does not help. Expand your message to include a visual clue such as color or location or simplify your message. Be careful not to use simple language all the time.

9) The child may have temper tantrums, sulk, whine, or carry on in some manner that you don't like. If the child is making a lot of noise he or she cannot hear you talk. Establish a touch to calm the child. If the child is having a tantrum, calmly take the hearing aids away before the child throws them. Isolate him or her until peace resumes. Hopefully this behavior will end soon.

10) If you are too far away from the child, he or she will not hear you when you speak. This is not willful misbehavior. If it appears the child is "playing deaf," move close to the child and repeat what you said. Give the benefit of doubt to the child in behavior issues where the child appears willful but may really have not heard you. For example: The wind obliterates speech outside.

11) In time of danger, do not expect the child to hear. Run to the child and grab him or her.

12) New babysitters should be prepared to spend extra time at the child's house getting to know the child before the parents go away.

13) Parents who have a child with hearing problems really need some time off. A good babysitter, who will learn a little about handling the child, and who will come back is worth his or her weight in gold.

14) Be fair to all the children.

Teachers and Schools

1) Effective mainstreaming requires individualized support services presented in an integrated, efficient, and accountable plan.

2) Teachers, schools, and school boards vary greatly. Some have lots of money and can do a great deal to help your child. Most do not. Suggest teacher training. Suggest smaller classes.

3) Parents can help the teacher to learn about hard-of-hearing children if the teacher or principal are willing to see the parent as a useful source of information. Collect short articles about hearing problems that are easily understood and pass them on to the teacher.

4) Children with mild hearing losses can seem to cope so well that they

fool people and consequently they may miss a lot. They tire easily because they work so hard at coping. Many children with mild hearing losses are considered "retarded," slow, or badly behaved. It is particularly necessary to explain this to teachers.

5) Learn how hearing aids and FM system work to make life easier in the classroom. Earshot distance limits the hearing aid. Questions from other children who often have quiet little voices should be repeated clearly by the teacher into the FM. The FM should be used in assemblies, on school excursions, and used by all teachers who teach the child. Teachers should learn the Ling Five-Sounds Test and to use it with the FM each morning, and when the FM is passed to another teacher.

6) Children with mild hearing losses should be seated within ten feet of the teacher's main teaching stand, and facing the teacher's full front face when possible. The teacher should not talk while writing on a blackboard. The teacher should not expect the child to listen while putting his head down on the desk.

7) While hoping the child will question what is not understood, never expect the child to know what he or she did not hear.

8) Children with mild hearing losses do better in a quiet classroom. A rug under the child's desk and/or sound baffles help to cut down on classroom noise. All children benefit from a quieter classroom.

9) Make sure there is a supply of hearing aid batteries at school, usually locked in the office.

Dangers and Emergencies

1) **Tiny hearing aid batteries are poisonous if swallowed.** Their acid eats into the stomach and the swallower can bleed to death in minutes. Go to a hospital immediately, one with full equipment, x-ray facilities, surgeon, and anesthetist, if the child swallows a battery or a hearing aid.

2) **Childproofing your home is vital**, even more vital when a child is hard of hearing. Keep all pills, hearing aid batteries (new and used), matches, and dangerous chemicals under lock and key, and keep the key out of reach.

3) **When the child is out of earshot you must always go and see what is going on.** You cannot call upstairs "What are you doing?" when there is an ominous silence. Try not to be too fierce.

4) **Teach the child to survive in a world of traffic.** Hold the child's hand on the street or in a parking lot. Constant training to stop, look both ways and listen will instill automatic self control that can save his life. Children on tricycles belong in backyards, behind fences, or on sidewalks, **never** on driveways or streets.

5) **Prevent Child Abuse.** Know your child's daily schedule, where he or she is and with whom he or she is alone on a regular basis. How well do you know these people? Talk to your child so that he or she will learn to be aware and take precautions. Teach your child to tell you what happens every day and listen to them.

6) **Teach the child to pick up the phone receiver in an emergency** and dial **911** or **0** for help. Teach him not to hang up so the line can stay open and be traced if the child was not understood. **Have at least one phone in the house and the school on which the child can hear.**

The phone does not go over the child's ear, but over the hearing aid with the microphone in the middle of the ear piece.

6) On Dealing with Professionals

1) Be prepared to share a history of the child since conception, plus family history at the beginning of each professional association. Use your own language, but have pertinent paper records available (medical, psychological, educational).

2) Parents know their own child well. Observe your child. Note comments of teachers and friends and date them for your records by the age of the child. Keep accurate and detailed records.

3) As soon as your child is diagnosed with a hearing problem, contact your school's special education office. Send copies of all hearing and speech testing to the special education office. When the child is ready for school, a complete file of all testing will be available.

4) Get your professional contacts to send you any reports on your child as well as a copy to your family doctor or pediatrician, the audiologist, speech pathologist, psychologist, and school board. A parent is the most important member of the team.

5) Question your professionals. Get them to give you guidelines. Make them explain everything in plain English, not their professional

jargon. In addition, a first-year textbook for auditory and speech pathology students may help you.

6) Be sure that all of your professionals know how to approach your child sucessfully. These visits must be positive.

7) Allow the child as much control as possible on these professional visits to let him or her feel less intimidated. For example, let the child choose a chair to sit in.

8) Try to choose a hearing aid dealer close to home. You will be making many trips for earmolds and broken hearing aids.

9) It is not what the professional does in a one-hour session, but what you do the rest of the time that has a lasting effect. A parent is the most useful tool a teacher or professional can have.

10) Be sure your speech pathologist knows the special problems of hearing impairment and knows what your child can and cannot hear.

7) On Audiograms, Measurements, and Definitions for Those With Hearing Impairments The Ling Five-Sounds Test

Audiograms

1) The audiogram is a chart of the sounds a person can hear in a perfect acoustic environment. Sound is a physical event which has three measurable components.

Frequency: the number of times a sound wave vibrates, measured in cycles per second (CPS or Hertz (Hz).

Intensity: how loud a sound is, measured in decibels (dB).

Duration: how long a sound lasts, not measured on an audiogram.

Speech sounds show on the audiogram in a banana-shaped area call the "**speech banana**" or CLEAR zone (Conversational Level Elements in the Acoustic Range of Speech)

Measurements and Definitions for Those with Hearing Impairments

1) **Hearing Loss:** Educators and professionals rank hearing loss in the

research-based terms of modern audiology. Audiologists rank hearing loss as:

Mild	(26dB to 30 dB)
Moderate	(31dB to 50dB)
Moderate to Severe	(31dB to 70 dB)
Severe to Profound	(71dB to 90dB)
Profound	(91dB or more)
Total	

These numerical values are based on the average of the hearing loss at three frequencies: 500 Hz, 1,000 Hz, and 2,000 Hz in the better ear without amplification.

2) **Hearing-Impaired:** Those with any degree of hearing loss from mild to profound.

3) **Hard of Hearing:** Usually a mild to moderate loss. A hearing impairment whether permanent or temporary which adversely affects a child's communication and education. The child is not deaf in the strict numerical sense of severe to profound loss. The linguistic development is primarily auditory-based with vision serving as a secondary and supplementary channel.

4) **Deaf:** A hearing impairment so severe that a child is impaired in processing linguistic information through hearing with or without amplification and which adversely affects educational performance. A prelingual primarily sensorineural bilateral hearing loss of 91dB or more. The communication development is visually based (either sign language or speech reading).

Any degree of hearing loss may limit full communicative access to educational opportunities in most schools without appropriate support.

The Ling Five-Sounds Test

1) The five sounds of the Ling Five-Sounds Test are based on the five sounds located within the **speech banana** or CLEAR zone. The sounds are **ah ee ou sh ss**. Teach the child to clap or repeat each sound when he hears you say them within earshot.

2) The Ling Five-Sounds Test is simple, cheap, and fast, and gives you an accurate picture of how the child is hearing that day while using his hearing aids. The Ling Test should also be used when the FM is hooked up at school each day. Many parents also use a password of

high-frequency sounds with easily confused words such as **fish-kiss**, **ash-ass**, **miss-mist**, **ketchup**, **cats spit**, **cats sit**, to extend the test.

The Child with a Mild Loss Who Does Not Have Hearing Aids

1) Test the child's hearing every day with the Ling Five-Sounds Test at twenty feet. Use a password comprised of high-frequency sounds:

    A. To see if the child is developing a middle ear infection.

    B. To ensure another day of good hearing so essential in building the foundation of language skills.

8) On the Ear and Hearing Aids, and Daily Nitty-Gritty Problems

The Ear

1) Keep the ear cannals and outer ear dry to prevent bacteria. Remove the hearing aids and wash earmolds several times a day if your child is prone to outer ear problems.

2) Check all drugs given to your child, especially ear drops that go in the ear canal, either prescription or over-the-counter medications to make sure they are not ototoxic which could cause further deafness especially if the child has ventilation tubes or a ruptured eardrum.

3) A child with ventilation tubes must not get his ears wet. Water in the ear canal goes through the eardrum via the tubes to cause infection. Get effective earplugs for swimming, bathing, showering, shampooing, wading pools, and even rainstorms.

4) An otoscope is better than a flashlight for looking into the ear. This is a professional tool for which your doctor can give you a prescription. If you cannot afford an otoscope, a flashlight will do, but find one which does not have a black circle in the middle of the light.

5) Get your doctor to show you what the ear canal should look like normally. If anything looks different than what you have been shown, take the child to the doctor.

6) If your flashlight shows that the eardrum at the back of the ear canal is grey/white, it is normal. If it is bright red; there is an infection or the child is or has been crying.

Earwax

1) Check with a flashlight for earwax build-up. It blocks sound from the hearing aid, and can cause a ruptured eardrum if the wax is pushed too far down the ear canal.

2) To get rid of earwax, use warm water and peroxide or warm water alone. Never deal with earwax yourself if the child has ventilation tubes. Take the child to the doctor.

Earmolds

1) From infancy to three years, earmolds might have to be replaced every six weeks. It slows down after that to about once a year by age eight. Get the best possible earmolds, usually made of a flexible material which is hypoallergenic.

2) Hearing aids on two ears means two earmolds, one for the left ear and one for the right. They are never interchangeable. Until you can tell them apart, mark which earmold goes in which ear.

3) Use lubrication to put the earmold into the ear if necessary. Use Vitamin E oil. Do not use Vaseline or mineral oil which eats the new earmold material.

4) Clean the earmolds with a mild soap and water. Get a rubber blower at a radio store and blow the tubing dry. Never use a hair dryer, microwave, toaster or oven.

5) Try to get new earmolds as fast as possible (within twenty-four hours) when new ones are needed. Turning down the volume on the hearing aid to stop the feedback does not give the child all the sound he or she needs to hear. Furthermore, the squealing sound of feedback can be highly irritating to everyone.

6) Feedback (squealing noise) may mean:
   A. A need for new earmolds (most common cause in babies and children)
   B. Wax in the ear canal
   C. A middle ear infection
   D. A broken casing on the hearing aid
   E. The hearing aid may need to be pushed in.

Middle Ear Infections (Otitis Media)

1) Children who wear hearing aids are prone to middle ear infections.

A child who has a middle ear infection can have a functional hearing loss up to a moderate loss.

2) Symptoms of middle ear infections include fever, pain severe enough to keep the child awake, rubbing or pulling at the ear, complaining of bubbles in the ear. The child should have an ear examination including a tympanogram.

3) Suggested medical treatment of recurrent middle ear infections include antibiotic and decongestant therapy for three months, surgery to install ventilation tubes, or doing nothing. Doing nothing can result in massive infections and further deafness.

4) Try to get a child with recurrent ear infections to "pop" his ears by yawning or swallowing every day.

5) For an unaided child with recurrent middle ear infections, use the Ling Five-Sounds Test, **ah ee ou sh ss** plus a changing password of high-frequency sounds, at twenty feet to determine if the child can hear as well as he or she should every day.

6) Be careful of nose blowing. Blowing too hard with one nostril blocked can force mucous up the eustachian tubes. Nose blowing should be supervised, otherwise the nose should be wiped.

Aids to Hearing

1) **Hearing aid:** An electronic device to amplify sound worn in the ear or on the body.

2) **FM System:** A frequency-modulated "radio" which increases speech sounds over surrounding background noise. This is useful in classrooms, cars, shopping malls, and any public place including auditoriums and concert halls. The speaker (a teacher or parent in public places where noise is a fact) wears a transmitter/microphone. The child wears a receiver. The system can be used alone or in conjunction with hearing aids or cochlear implants.

3) **Cochlear Implant:** An electronic implant into the inner ear. Sounds are converted into electrical currents which are used to stimulate the remaining hearing nerve endings in the cochlea and generate sensations of hearing. These sensations have to be translated into speech sounds through special training. Cochlear Implants are only as successful as the training programs and education provided with them. Cochlear implants are for those with profound sensorineural hearing impairment, who cannnot understand language through hearing aids.

Hearing Aids and the Child

1) Have a bag to keep together, hearing aids, cases, batteries, crochet hook, small flashlight or otoscope, and Vitamin E oil. Hearing aids can be in the parent's hand, the child's ears or in the hearing aid bag. Nowhere else. The bag should be kept under lock and key because of the batteries.

2) Two ears means two hearing aids. Hearing aids are custom-tuned for each ear, and are never interchangeable.

3) Treat hearing aids happily. Flaunt them. Choose hearing aids in bright colors if the child wants. Decorate FM systems with stickers.

4) To get your child to leave the hearing aids in his or her ears, do the following:

   A. Tell the child how great the hearing aids are and believe it yourself.

   B. Try to have ready curious little sounds which the child can only hear with the hearing aids in, like a music box in a stuffed animal. Let the child listen.

   C. Use Kiddi-hooks.

   D. Use adhesive tape between the child's scalp and the hearing aid.

   E. Be patient.

   F. Use candy (i.e., a carrot stick in each hand while putting in the hearing aids).

   G. If the child continues to be difficult, a recheck with the audiologist is in order.

   H. Never forget who is supposed to be the boss. Be firm, and don't feel sorry for the child or yourself.

   I. Make a harness like a reading glasses chain, pinned to the back of the babies shirt so that the hearing aid will not be lost even if the baby takes it out. Dental floss works.

5) When the child is old enough, around age four, let the child learn to put in the hearing aids without a mirror so that he can handle them anywhere, even in the dark.

6) It is essential that the child hear well every day. Hearing aids are useless if they are not fully functioning. Check the hearing aid every night:

   A. With the Ling-Five-Sounds Test.

   B. By listening to conversation at maximum earshot.

    C. By a quick evaluation of general background noise.

    D. A weak hearing aid battery will not make it through the day. Change to a fresh battery.

7) When the hearing aid is new, get a copy of the electronic output function (shown on its testing strip) and use it as a baseline to compare its functioning when it gets older.

8) BTE aids are fragile. Don't drop them or get them wet. Cracks can cause irregular feedback. Water can cause distortion to the sound, several days after getting them wet.

9) On Teaching Aids: Toys, Books, Phones, Computers etc.

Talking, arguing, debating, discussing, commenting, lecturing, whining, snivelling, shouting, whispering, teasing, explaining, demonstrating, rambling, joking, retorting, chatting, gossiping, conferring, conversing, singing, haranguing, jabbering, muttering, prattling, preaching, ranting, reasoning, spouting, tattling, fibbing, blaming, resolving, blabbing, chattering, mediating, consulting, and forgiving. This is the communication within the family which the child takes part in with every family member every day. This is more important than any other single factor. It is the most essential teaching aid. However, the child must have properly functioning hearing aids, otherwise the child cannot hear it nor take part in it.

TV

1) The TV can be a wonderful teaching aid for language.

2) The hard-of-hearing child who lipreads cannot lipread a puppet, or a cartoon. Provide guidance through the Saturday morning cartoons because the child may only be watching the visual action, and not listening which is a waste of time.

3) The hard-of-hearing child may choose to sit about two-to-three feet away from the television or turn the TV up too loud. Consider buying a patch cord to attach the hearing aid to the television, or a set of headphones.

4) Closed Captioning for TV, if available, can be very helpful for the child with hearing problems and promotes reading skills for all the family.

5) A VCR is helpful because it allows repetition of programs for learning purposes as well as viewing at a convenient time and previewing for content.

Toys

1) A toy should be something you think your child will want to play with and enjoy. If you can see a secondary aspect for language learning, that is wonderful. Toy cars are great for color sorting and vehicle identification.

2) The more shapes a toy can assume the better. Building blocks can be varied infinitely. A parent with a sharp knife can turn a lowly cardboard box into anything.

3) Toys aimed at replacing a parent's voice such as Teddy Ruxpin may not have good enough voice quality for the child to hear clearly. Buy more books and forget the talking bear. Read to the child yourself.

4) Many public libraries have toys and books, and longer lending times for children with impaired hearing.

5) You need at least one special toy for teaching play audiometry such as stacking rings or put a piece in a puzzle at a specific sound.

6) Play audiometry is used for children between two and four years when they easily get bored during the testing process. Play audiometry is teaching the child to do something when he or she hears a tone. Parents practice this at home, which helps the audiologist at hearing test time.

Books

1) Be comfortable with your choice of reading material. You will read out loud with more excitement.

2) Reading skills may lag when the child has hearing problems. The child must be able to hear and feel himself say the speech sounds so as to relate them to the alphabet letters which represent them on the page. A child needs to hear a word about ten times to learn it. A hard-of-hearing child needs more repetition to attain this same learning.

3) Also, to help the child remember better, transpose words from the book into his or her world. When they are thirsty draw their attention to words in the book such as: 'thirsty,' 'juice,' or 'bottle.'

Memory Books

1) A memory book is made to discuss what happened today. They are great vocabulary builders. Many parents with enough artistic talent to do a stick person have created great memory books. Other members of the family can do the memory books too, and provide a different focus. Photos which are family album rejects also help the child remember words associated with events. A video camera can be used to provide memory books such as the child at the zoo with ten animals and all the sounds. Video cameras can also be used to record speech progress.

Books for Teaching Vocabulary (Aural Books)

1) An aural book should have no more than eight pages for a child who is one-to-three years old. Each page should be a clear drawing of one object on a plain background. You see the picture, you say the word while the child listens, the child says it, then looks at the picture. The words should be appropriate for the child's world.

2) There are some limited vocabulary books meant for early readers which are very useful when the child's vocabulary grows beyond twenty words at age two. Keep these books until the child has used them twice, once as aural books and once as early readers.

Computers

1) Try to pick computer games which reinforce interactive action with other humans like Scrabble rather than solitary silent endeavors like "Tetris." Mysteries "Lost in Time" can be used either way, if the whole family attempts to play cooperatively, and discusses the issues or clues at dinner.

2) Make sure your computer is absolutely silent. When the printer is working, the child may not be able to hear near the computer.

3) Put in the best quality sound package in you can afford. It is the way of the future anyway, but the child must have a better than average sound quality to listen to even if he or she is just playing games.

"Real Time" Learning

1) Allow the child to help you in the kitchen. Think of the vocabulary

possibilities in how to cook, what to cook, how long, and how much. Let the child make cookies shaped like butterflies, turtles, or airplanes. Cut sandwiches into a million shapes.

2) Always use an open question such as "What kind of sandwich do you want for lunch? Peanut butter or bologna?" which provides modeling and choice, while still controlling the options.

3) Assess every moment of the day to cull the opportunities to work on the sound targets of the week. When the child is successful, reward him or her with a hug. When the child is not successful, quickly add on another challenge which you know will be successful and reward the child with a hug.

4) Don't work on speech for longer than two-to-three minutes at a time.

5) Find something the child can do really well, focus on this talent and nurture it. Instead of talking about the child with hearing problems all the time, talk about the child who grows great marigolds, runs well, swims, paints, or tells great stories.

10) On Meeting the Costs of Hearing Problems

1) Tell people if you need financial aid. If you don't tell them, they will assume you don't need it. Ask your audiologist if he or she knows of any charitable or service organization which might help you buy hearing aids.

2) Insure the hearing aids. This may be difficult, but even at high rates, insurance covers the astronomical replacement cost.

3) Keep careful records of all medical expenses, with receipts and dates. Keep receipts for all equipment: hearing aids, FM systems, earmolds, batteries, etc. for tax purposes. (Keep all warranty cards.) Get doctors to certify the purposes of expenses: i.e. cure, alleviation, prevention, treatment and/or the dysfunction of your child's condition.

United States Tax Deductions

1) In the United States, you are entitled to tax deductions for medical expenses for a child who is hard-of-hearing if your expenses are more than 7.5 percent of your gross adjusted income.

The following items may be deductible:

A. Cost of educational services, special instruction in lipreading or sign language, speech therapy, auditory-verbal therapy.

B. Equipment and supplies: hearing aids, FM units, telephone/teletype equipment and repair, television adapter for closed captioning.

C. Hospital services: lab exams, tests, medical treatments, etc.

D. Professional services: speech therapist, psychologist, etc.

E. Transportation to and from: special schools, hospitals, clinics, pathologists, specialists and pharmacists.

Contact:

The Family Resource Center on Disabilities

20 East Jackson Boulevard, Room 900

Chicago, IL 60604 U.S.A.

Tel: (312) 939-3513

Or

Internal Revenue Service

Tel: (1-800) 829-1040

Canada Federal Tax Deductions

1) The Canadian Income Tax Department is less than willing to give parents of children with disabilities a break. If your child's leg is cut off, it only counts if the amputation is above the knee. For parents to claim the child as hearing impaired, and receive a special deduction, the child must be unable to speak or use a telephone. A doctor has to fill out the form stating the child has a **severe long-term** disability. In Canada, you will not get this for a hard-of-hearing child with a mild loss. If your child has a moderate loss and you get a deduction, put the money in the bank until the department wants it back. Be prepared to be audited, to have your properly filled-out forms denied by the department and for the department to change its mind about your child's status.

2) Every year the Canadian government issues bulletins of bona fide tax deductions. If you purchase a closed captioner or TTY, keep the receipts for income tax purposes. Batteries for hearing aids, the parent's share of hearing aid purchases and repairs and earmolds, mileage to get to experts (under certain circumstances) are medical deductions regardless of the degree of hearing loss, but financial

advice is needed. Contact the Canadian Income Tax Department for new information each year.

Ontario Ministry of Health, Assistive Devices Plan

1) In Canada, medical care is socialized. In Ontario, the province where I live, the Minister of Health has a plan called Assistive Devices Plan or ADP. ADP provides universal financial aid to pay for three-fourths of the price of one pair of hearing aids and one pair of earmolds, once every three years for children under eighteen.

2) In Ontario, the government provides limited access to speech pathologists, audiologists, and auditory-verbal therapists in hospitals for preschoolers and in schools for children of school age.

Ontario Handicapped Children's Allowance

1) This fund is doled out by the Ontario Minister of Social Services to help with the cost of special services related to the child's hearing problems. It has a limit on income levels it will assist and a sliding scale. (The more you earn, the less you can get.) If you are a single mother struggling with a job and a child it will pay for contract workers to enhance the child's day care and will provide respite for you. It is based on your previous year's income. Handicapped Children's Allowance can sometimes be used to educate the parents or to buy books.

The kind of information provided on Ontario's Handicapped Children's Allowance is the kind of information which is important for parents of hard-of-hearing children in many countries. Some countries will have better help for parents. Some will have none at all.

You usually have to apply for help, and you may have to do some intensive digging to even find out about such help, no matter where you live.

Bibliography

Berres, Michael S., and Knoblock, Peter, (Eds), (1987) *Program Models for Mainstreaming: Integrating Students with Moderate to Severe Disabilities.* Rockville, MD: Aspen Publishing. (Chapter 8. Marian K. Hesseltine. "A Model for Public School Programming for Hearing Impaired Students." pp 141–169)

Bombeck, Erma, (1989) *I Want to Grow Hair, I Want to Grow Up, I Want to Go to Boise: Children Surviving Cancer.* New York: Harper & Row.

Brazelton, T. Berry, MD., (1987) *What Every Baby Knows.* Reading, MA: Addison-Wesley.

Brinkley, Ginny and Linda Goldberg, and Janice Kukar, 2nd Ed. (1988) *Your Child's First Journey: A Guide to Prepared Birth from Pregnancy to Parenthood.* Garden City Park, N. Y.: Avery. (Chapter 10. "The Newborn: or There'll be Some Changes Made." pp. 149–171)

Castle, Diane L., "The Oral Interpreter." Carol Lee De Filippo. Donald G. Sims. (Eds,) (1988) **New Reflections on Speechreading.** *The Volta Review,* 90, 5.

Colley, David, (1985) *Sound Waves: The True Story of a Deaf Child Who Learned to Hear Using a Revolutionary Teaching Method. (Beebe).* New York: St Martin's. Press.

Courtman-Davies, Mary, (1979) *Your Deaf Child's Speech and Language.* London: Bodley Head.

Flexer, Carol, (1990) "Audiological Rehabilitation in the Schools." *American Speech-Language-Hearing Association.* **ASHA**. April, 1990.

Flexer, Carol, Denise Wray and JoAnn Ireland. (1989) "Preferential Seating is Not Enough: Issues in Classroom Management of Hearing-Impaired Students." *Language, Speech and Hearing Services in Schools.* Rockville, MD: American Speech-Language-Hearing Assocation 20, 11–21.

Gordon, Thomas Ph.D., (1989) *Teaching Children Self-Discipline at Home and at School: New Ways Parents and Teachers Can Build Self-Control, Self-Esteem and Self-Reliance.* New York: Times Books.

Hoff, Benjamin, (1982) *The Tao of Pooh.* New York: Penguin Books.

Kitzinger, Sheila, (1986) *Being Born.* Photography by Lennart Nilsson. London: Penguin Books.

Ledson, Sidney, (1975) *Teach Your Child to Read in 64 Days.* New York: Norton.

Lewis, C. S., (1953) *The Silver Chair.* Illustrations by Pauline Baynes. London: Bles. pp. 40–44.

Ling, Daniel, Ph.D., Agnes Ling Phillips, Ph.D., (1978). *Aural Habilitation: The Foundations of Verbal Learning.* Washington DC.: Alexander Graham Bell Association for the Deaf.

Ling, Daniel, Ph.D. (Ed). (1984) *Early Intervention for Hearing-Impaired Children: Oral Options.* San Diego, CA: College Hill Press.

Ling, Daniel, Ph.D. (1989) *Foundations of Spoken Language for Hearing-Impaired Children.* Wash DC: Alexander Graham Bell Assocation for the Deaf.

Ling, Daniel, Ph.D. (1976) *Speech and the Hearing-Impaired Child: Theory and Practice*. Washington DC.: Alexander Graham Bell Association for the Deaf.

Long, William Stuart, (1982) **The Australians**, Vol. IV, *The Explorers*. (Dickon) New York, New York: Dell.

Martin, Frederick N. (1991) *Introduction to Audiology*, 4th Ed. (1991) Englewood Cliffs, NJ: Prentice-Hall.

Marty, David R., M.D. (1987) *The Ear Book: A Parent's Guide to Common Ear Disorders of Children*. Jefferson City, MO: Lang ENT.

McArthur, Shirley Hanawalt. (1982) *Raising Your Hearing-Impaired Child: A Guidebook for Parents*. Washington DC.: Alexander Graham Bell Association for the Deaf.

McGuiness, Diane, (1985) *When Children Don't Learn: Understanding the Biology and Psychology of Learning Disorders*. New York: Basic Books

Milne, A. A. (1924) *When We Were Very Young*. New York: E. P. Dutton.

Milne, A. A. (1926) *Winnie Ille Pu*. Translated by Alexander Lenard (1960) New York: E. P. Dutton.

Northern, Jerry L. Ph. D, and Marion P. Downs, M. A., *Hearing in Children*, 2nd Ed (1978) Baltimore, MD: Williams & Wilkins.

Northern, Jerry L. and Marion P. Downs. *Hearing in Children*, 4th Ed. (1991) Baltimore, MD: Williams & Wilkins.

Ontario: Ministry of Education; Program Implementation & Review Branch. (1989) *Review of Ontario Education Programs for Deaf and Hard of Hearing Students*. Toronto, Ontario (Canada): Ontario Ministry of Education.

Sacks, Oliver, (1989) *Seeing Voices: A Journey into the World of the Deaf.* Berkeley, CA: University of California Press.

Schwartz, Sue, Ed. (1987) *Choices in Deafness: A Parent's Guide*. Rockville, MD: Woodbine House.

Schwartz, Sue, Ph.D. and Joan E. Heller Miller, (1988) *The Language of Toys: Teaching Communication Skills to Special Needs Children/A Guide for Parents and Teachers.* Rockville MD: Woodbine House.

Scott, Dorothy, with Nana Ho, (1979) *Join in Learning to Listen.* Toronto, Canada: VOICE for Hearing-Impaired Children.

Simon, Sarina, Ed. with Susan Amerikaner and Susan Dichter, (1989) *101 Amusing Ways to Develop your Child's Thinking Skills and Creativity.* Los Angeles, CA: Lowell House.

Spock, Benjamin, M.D. (1988) *Dr. Spock on Parenting: Sensible Advice from America's Most Trusted Child-Care Expert.* New York: Simon & Schuster.

Steel, Danielle, (1982) *Once upon a Lifetime.* New York: Dell.

Sternberg, Martin L. A. (1990) *American Sign Language Concise Dictionary.* New York: Harper & Row.

U.S. Office of Medical Applications of Research, National Institute on Deafness and other Communication Disorders, National Institute of Child Health and Human Development, National Institute of Neurologial Disorders and Stroke. *Consensus Conference on Early Identification of Hearing Impairment in Infants and Young Children.* Bethesda, Maryland, March 1–3, 1993. Conference papers.

Vaughan, Pat, Ed. (1981) *Learning to Listen: A Book by Mothers for Mothers of Hearing-Impaired Children.* Toronto, Canada: VOICE for Hearing-Impaired Children.

Periodicals

VOICE-Audition. Toronto, Canada: VOICE for Hearing-Impaired Children.

The Volta Review. Washington DC.: Alexander Graham Bell Association for the Deaf.

Volta Voices. Washington DC.: Alexander Graham Bell Association for the Deaf, International Parents Organization.

Exceptional Parent. Brookline, MA: Psy-Ed Corp.

Index

The Candlish Family. Left to Right: William, Reid (our Hero), Barbara, PAM, Ross, and Tiffany.
Drawing by Reid Candlish (age five years).